KU-358-924

BRITISH AGRICULTURE

A Report of an Inquiry organized by

VISCOUNT ASTOR and **B. SEEBOHM ROWNTREE**

PUBLISHER'S NOTE

If you are not already on our mailing list and would
like to know when new books are added, please
send in your name and address on a postcard.
Suggestions for new additions are welcomed.

BRITISH AGRICULTURE

The Principles of Future Policy

A Report of an Inquiry organized by

VISCOUNT ASTOR

and

B. SEEBOHM ROWNTREE

PUBLISHED AS A 'PELICAN SPECIAL' BY
PENGUIN BOOKS LIMITED
HARMONDSWORTH MIDDLESEX ENGLAND

First Published 1939

MADE AND PRINTED IN GREAT BRITAIN FOR PENGUIN BOOKS LIMITE
BY PURNELL AND SONS, LTD., PAULTON (SOMERSET) AND LONDON

PREFACE

In 1934 we organized an inquiry into the possibilities of land settlement as a method of relieving unemployment. We were helped by:—

SIR ROBERT GREIG, formerly Permanent Secretary of the Scottish Department of Agriculture, a member of the Livestock Commission, and for a time of the Bacon Development Board, who had had a wide experience of farming in the United Kingdom, in the British Empire and on the Continent;

SIR FREDERICK KEEBLE, F.R.S., formerly Professor of Botany at Oxford, Assistant Secretary of the English Ministry of Agriculture and Agricultural Adviser to Imperial Chemical Industries, Ltd.;

MR. H. D. HENDERSON, a member of the Economic Advisory Council and Fellow of All Souls;

MR. WILLIAM WALLACE, an economist, who had taken part in various social investigations; and

MISS DOREEN WARRINER, Lecturer in Economics, University College, London, who co-operated in the Survey of World Agriculture undertaken by the Royal Institute of International Affairs.

MR. P. LAMARTINE YATES, an economist, who acted as secretary to the Group.

After a year's investigation, our conclusions were published under the title of "*The Agricultural Dilemma*."

We had been led to make that inquiry by a sense of the need for a strictly objective examination of the subject. Our survey led us, to our general regret, to conclusions which were negative and pessimistic so far as that particular subject was concerned. That limited investigation, however, necessarily involved us in some consideration of a variety of important problems concerned with the future of British agriculture. We were surprised to find how meagre was the information available on many of them, how far the student was dependent upon views which were partial or partisan, or biased by vested interests. Yet it was clear that, with other countries, our agriculture was passing through a critical period of transition and experiment, and that decisions of far-reaching importance would have to be made in the immediate future, especially the major decision as to whether there should be any reorientation in policy. It seemed to us, therefore, that a wise solution of the various problems concerned with future policy as a coherent whole must be helped by a systematic inquiry, which would take due account both of the technical factors relating to agricultural development and of the broader social, economic, and political considerations necessarily involved.

With this in view, we decided to continue our investigations. We invited Mr. James Keith, a well-known farmer in Scotland and England, to join us. But the Group was only a focal point for the collection of technical information and the views of agricultural and other experts. By personal interviews, by *ad hoc* inquiries, by conference and by correspondence, we have drawn upon the knowledge and the criticisms of many of the leading experts of this country, including the agricultural economists associated with the universities and agricultural colleges and institutes. In parenthesis we desire to pay a very warm tribute to the ungrudging help we have had from so many in the course of the inquiry. The names of some will be found at the end of this Preface.

While, however, we record our thanks for the great help received, we must make it clear that the Group are alone responsible for the views set out in our publication "British Agriculture." Moreover, whilst there is general agreement in the Group itself, it does not follow that each individual accepts every minor statement made in the book.

"British Agriculture" was published in September 1938.

It had a very good reception in the press and satisfactory sales, especially considering that its price was 15s. and its size 469 pages.

This Penguin edition will give the public a shorter and cheaper book and also one which has been brought up to date. We reproduce in full and practically verbatim Chapters 1 to 3 (which give a survey of the past and the objectives for the future) and Chapter 23 (with our conclusions). The intermediate Chapters 4 to 22 inclusive have been summarized and brought up to date: they deal with each commodity separately as well as with such matters as the agricultural worker, the small holder, the farmer, the landlord and agricultural credit, and the important subject of research and education, dealt with in Chapter 22. This Preface not only contains the material which was in the Preface of the original volume but also refers to some points not dealt with there.

Owing to lack of time it has not been possible to submit the proofs of this edition to all our colleagues. We believe they would agree to our summaries, revisions and additions which bring the book up to date, but we alone assume responsibility for the contents of the Penguin edition in so far as they vary from the fuller volume.

While preparing this book we, like all others, worked under the cloud of the threat of war. Discussions were necessarily conducted in the context of war-preparedness, with the knowledge that war would compel us to increase home output of agricultural produce regardless of cost. Even the possibility of war made it necessary for the Government to take certain precautionary measures for storing food and augmenting the output of certain foods-measures that would not be necessary in a normal world. But a return to a world order of peace and confidence, accompanied by a demobilisation of the war machine in this and other countries, is only possible if accompanied by a rapid and developing resumption of international trade. Our proposals accordingly are intended not only to bring stability and prosperity to British agriculture and to advance social welfare by a frontal attack on the evils of malnutrition, but also to contribute to improved international relationships by an increased exchange of goods and services.

Until 1931, Free Trade and *laisser-faire* were the guiding principles of our commercial policy, and the attitude of the State towards agriculture was governed by these considerations. In 1931 Free Trade was abandoned. At the same time there was a catastrophic fall in world food prices. One branch of agriculture after another was faced with grave difficulties. One by one *ad hoc* measures were introduced to avert ruin or help particular groups of farmers out of difficulties. In fact, this procedure had been begun soon after the Armistice.

When protection by means of a tariff was adopted for industry it was obvious that some balancing help would have to be given to farmers. Owing to the recollection of past political controversies over "food taxes", those who were responsible shunned the straight tariff for most foods and introduced quotas. Other reasons may also have helped towards this, among them the fact that overseas producers could, through depreciation of currencies or subsidising exports, surmount tariff duties; that the adoption of a system of control over overseas supplies enabled the Government to control domestic supplies also; and lastly, that the adoption of Marketing Schemes with the resulting control over domestic production enabled the Government to demand a similar power of controlling imports and thereby to set aside certain commercial treaties.

In applying both quotas and tariffs the aim is to raise the price of the domestic product or to prevent it from falling. When the quota system was adopted politicians probably did not, and the public certainly did not, realise that they might in some cases prove to be a more severe "food tax" (i.e. to be more costly to consumers) than tariff duties.

Of recent years the relative effect of quotas and tariffs on international trade and the standard of living has been examined by more than one international body. A few quotations serve to illustrate some of the conclusions reached.

"If you use oil that is slightly too thick in the delicate mechanism of your watch, the watch will merely go slow; if you put your finger in, the watch will stop. That is, roughly speaking and with due allowance for all exceptions, the difference between duties and quotas as regards the operation of the balance of payments."
  (Economic Committee of the League of Nations, 1935.
  "Remarks on the Present Phase of International
      Economic Relations.")

"A revision of the measures taken to counteract depression is imperative, and it may be affirmed *a priori* that many quotas have now lost their justification."

"A moderate tariff will not constitute so rigid an impediment to trade as quotas."

"Only by such measures (as the enlargement and ultimate abandonment of agricultural quotas) will it be possible to protect the consumer against exploitation and to prevent the reduction in the standard of living of the people."
  (Economic Committee of the League of Nations, 1937.
  "The Present Phase of International Economic
      Relations.")

One further point—with tariffs a contribution is made to the Treasury. The extent to which this is paid by the overseas producer depends on many factors which may vary in the case of different commodities, the period of time, the amount of world output and the quantity of the domestic supply compared to imports. But with a quota no contribution at all is made to the Treasury by the overseas producer.

Quotas are intended to divide the home market, guaranteeing a share or quota to the home producer and a share or quota to the overseas producer. Theoretically each section is given a slice of the market in which competition from the other section is greatly reduced. The result has been that in certain cases the overseas producer has been able to raise his price without corresponding benefit to the home producer—in other words to compel consumers to subsidise overseas producers to a greater extent than domestic producers. This happened with the Bacon and Beef Quotas.

Bulk purchase by the Government of agricultural commodities has been suggested by some as an alternative means of helping home farmers, stabilising prices and securing adequate supplies. By this method the Government, or a body set up by the Government, would buy the entire domestic crop at a price which would give a profit to home producers and would then obtain any requirements in excess of domestic production from other sources at the ruling world price and sell the total of domestic and imported supplies to consumers at a price representing an average between the two.

One serious objection against this is that if the State undertook such transactions there would be a grave risk of its becoming involved in difficulties with the Dominions and other friendly countries, as well as cutting across existing trade agreements and treaties. Nothing would be more likely to break up goodwill within the Empire than for the British Government to buy the domestic crop of such a commodity as wheat at a price remunerative to the British farmer at a time when world wheat prices had slumped, and simultaneously to buy Dominion wheat at the lower world price. While they would expect individual grain merchants to buy in the cheapest markets, Dominion farmers would with reason complain against a discrimination by the British Government which meant ruin to them whilst guaranteeing a higher and a remunerative price to domestic growers.

After the adoption of Protection and of State intervention the need for a carefully considered constructive policy increased, yet though Governments of different political complexion have passed agricultural measures, no comprehensive, balanced policy has been formulated. The measures adopted have been of the nature of "first aid," or based on theory unsupported by facts. The time is now overdue for the nation to agree on a sound policy. We have endeavoured to consider what this should be.

Naturally there is a strong body of conservatively minded opinion and vested interests in favour of maintaining things very much as they are. At no time would such a policy be adequate, but to-day it is particularly inappropriate, because, as we endeavour to show, we are passing through a period of Agricultural Revolution comparable with the Industrial Revolution. Great changes in technique are taking place all over the world, and British agricultural policy must take account of them.

Again the suggestion is made, and carries much conviction, that our aim must be to increase the number of those engaged in agriculture, or at any rate to prevent further decline. This has been dealt with in *The Agricultural Dilemma*. We have re-examined with sympathy the thesis that agriculture deserves quite exceptional help, because it is an industry different in kind from urban industries in that it produces citizens physically, and in many ways, mentally and spiritually, healthier than those produced in the towns. Although the experience of other countries goes to prove that the rural population tends to give stability to a State, yet it is difficult to support this general thesis without qualifications. In any case, it requires that we provide standards of life, in terms of wages, housing, health, and education more nearly comparable with those enjoyed by the city population. It would seem as important to raise the standard of living in agriculture as to increase or preserve the numbers engaged. To do both might involve a prohibitive cost. Actually, the shrinkage of numbers employed in British agriculture is a tendency found in all progressive nations. As technique improves, the numbers required to produce the primary foodstuffs are necessarily reduced. If the proportion of the total population employed in British agriculture is less than in most other countries, this may not be a sign of decay but, on the contrary, a measure of a higher level of development and a higher standard of life. We value to the full the special qualities associated with land-workers and recognize the immense satisfaction and benefit derived from contact with the land. We desire to make it possible for as many as feasible to obtain that advantage, including the bringing of urban and industrial workers into closer contact with the country and food production. Yet we feel bound to state that no adequate agricultural policy can be based on a mere maintenance of numbers. Nor must the prosperity of food production in Britain be gauged by the acreage under cereals. In spite of the shrinkage in arable acreage and of the large acreage withdrawn from all forms of farming for urban and industrial development, our gross output of food to-day is greater than it was both in 1908, when the first census of Agricultural Production was made, and in 1870, when the arable acreage was much greater.

Again, it is urged that purely economic considerations must be subordinated to those of national defence, and that to safeguard the nation in war we must at once adopt measures not economically justifiable. We also dealt with this question in *The Agricultural Dilemma*, and we examine it once more in the following pages. We cannot be blind to the risk of war. It is right that we should insure against it. It is a question, however, of the best form of insurance. To us, as a nation, our financial and commercial strength and our widespread business relationships with other nations are likely to be of prime importance in war, or in the successful attempt to prevent war. Again, the size of our shipping and shipbuilding industries depends largely on the volume of our import trade in peace time. Our great Mercantile Marine was a vital factor in the last war and is likely to be no less vital should war occur in the future.

The question of the peace-time cost of self-sufficiency during war is also important. In war-time the public is willing to accept a lower standard of living and tighten its belt, but it would be unwise to demand excessive and unnecessary sacrifices in normal times. It is often confusedly argued that if we bought all our food supplies in Britain the money spent on these purchases would go to the British farmer and farm-worker, who would spend it on British manufactures, thus compensating us for the loss of our export trade. Sometimes it is even claimed that £100,000,000 more could advantageously be spent on home-produced food which now goes into the pockets of overseas producers. This reasoning might be correct if the costs of home-grown and imported foods were the same. But with many commodities the prices are widely apart.

In the 1936–7 season we produced about 10¾ million cwt. of sugar in this country and imported about 44 million cwt. How did this home sugar compare in cost with the imported? A cwt. of sugar imported from Cuba cost about 16s., including the duty, in this country. To encourage the home producer to compete at this price, the Government paid a subsidy of 4s. 9d. per cwt, and relieved home-produced sugar from duty to the equivalent of about 5s. per cwt. Therefore 9s. 9d. per cwt. or over 1d. per lb. represents approximately the difference between growing sugar in this country and importing it. The same is true of wheat; in 1935–6, we paid the British farmer 9s. 1d. per cwt. for wheat whose market price, determined by the price of imported wheat, was only 5s. 9d. This cost the country about £5,000,000 in that year; at which cost we were able to increase our self-sufficiency in wheat only from about 16 per cent to 25 per cent.

It is true that we might spend £100,000,000 more on home-produced instead of on imported food, but if the quantity so purchased was only worth say, £80,000,000 or £60,000,000 (in terms of imported supplies) then obviously consumers would be getting £20,000,000 or £40,000,000 less of foodstuffs for their expenditure.

The "self-sufficiency" line of argument is also based on the fundamental fallacy that one market can be exchanged for another like any mass-produced commodity. It assumes that the British export industries, if deprived of their markets overseas, can readily find a substitute market in the person of the British farmer—if only the export industries and the consuming public will provide the British farmer with purchasing power by buying British agricultural produce. Unfortunately for this contention, the British farmer (even if he had the purchasing power) simply does not want to buy the kind of goods (steel rails, machine tools, loco- motives, etc.) which account for the most valuable part of our present exports to countries overseas. The British farmer cannot be made to step into the shoes of the overseas customer because they do not fit.

So a policy approaching in normal times to agricultural self-sufficiency, or which damaged certain vital interests, would weaken rather than strengthen our position in war. Moreover, the choice is unnecessary, because the needed insurance can be better provided by a policy of reserves. These reserves would be firstly a sufficient stock of essential foodstuffs, such as wheat, sugar, maize, to tide us, with the help of our ships, over the first period; secondly, a reserve of fertility in our soil which could be drawn upon during the emergency period; and lastly, our livestock which could be treated as a reserve and slaughtered at need.

There is nothing in the defence aspect to prevent us from adopting an agricultural policy justified on other grounds. We should apply to agriculture the same standards as those applied to other industries: if it has in the past been unfairly treated it is entitled to redress: the present financial assistance afforded to it should not be diminished, but if it were redistributed both agriculture and the consumers would benefit.

Some have criticised us for not having dealt adequately in our earlier volume with what is called Bio-Dynamic Farming and the Indore Process or the importance of humus or organic manure. We have accordingly made a point of consulting some of the most representative and independent authorities on the subject. The claims made by supporters of this school briefly appear to be, firstly that an essential condition for obtaining the best quality in food, is the treatment of the soil with *organic* manure, whilst the lack of such *organic* manure impoverishes the soil to such an extent that animals and human beings eating foods grown on it suffer in health and physique; secondly, that disease is increasing among human beings and that this increase is due to the larger use of artificial fertilisers or to the irregular application, or to the non-application, of humus; and thirdly, that the consumption of grain and legumes grown on soil treated with organic manure (compost or humus) produces an improvement in health and physique which is measurable and augments resistance to infection.

Now, no one would deny the desirability of maintaining a proper organic content of the soil, and that humus certainly plays an important part in preserving this. But to admit this is far removed from accepting the statement, that human disease is increasing and that this is due to food having been grown in soil where artificial fertilisers have been used, or to food having been grown in soil where no natural manure has been applied.

The evidence to substantiate these claims seems inadequate and certainly all the vital statistics seem to indicate that disease among human beings, far from increasing, is decreasing. There is no doubt that crops grown in soil very deficient in certain minerals will become deficient in these constituents, and animals fed exclusively on these crops will in their turn become deficient and may become ill if these constituents are lacking. This is, for instance, true for aphosphorosis in horses, cattle, sheep and goats, a disease known all over the world in animals living on crops deficient in phosphorus.

Bad farming obviously will lead to a loss of fertility of the soil. But it has not yet been proved that the use of "compost" necessarily denotes good farming or better quality food.

Compost adds plant food, e.g., lime, phosphorus, etc., and adds humus which helps to retain moisture. But any artificial means of supplying these nutrients in the form of inorganic substances might have the same effect upon the plant as these nutrients supplied in the form of compost, and any kind of material which would help to retain moisture might have the same effect as the cellulose in the compost.

Experiments have been conducted at Rothamsted in which wheat was grown on three plots of ground which had organic manure, chemical manure, and no manure respectively. No difference in quality of the grain could be noted, though this does not necessarily mean that the results would be the same if the experiments were carried out for a longer period.

While, of course, there is much still unknown, there seems to be no evidence of any mysterious substances or quality in compost or humus which would affect the health value of plants other than nutrients which could be applied by the ordinary commercial fertilisers.

It is to be hoped that some scientific body will study and report on the whole question of the use of humus and that, if necessary, further experiments will be carried out. Otherwise the case for a sound nutrition policy based on a balanced dietary, which includes a sufficient quantity of the protective foods, gets confused in the public mind with the question as to whether the quality of both protective and energy foods can be, and is being, seriously affected by the conditions under which they are grown to-day in most countries, including Britain.

Let us now return to an examination of the basic principles of policy.

What, in the widest national interests, should agriculture produce ? and on what terms ? and under what conditions ? If for the moment (and without pressing the analogy unduly) we may regard the total economic activities in these islands as those of one great business enterprise, what is to be produced by the Food Production Department of that business, on what terms and how ?

The answer must not be dictated solely in the interests

of the consumer. Equally, however, it must not be determined solely in those of the producer, though full consideration must be given to his just rights and claims; the nation cannot properly ask that those engaged in the agricultural branch of the National Business should enjoy a position, all things considered, inferior to those in other branches. Steady supplies of good-quality food will not be forthcoming unless those engaged in its production are offered a return for effort comparable with that enjoyed in other industries. Equally the producers must recognize that in a democracy where consumers are overwhelmingly preponderant in numbers, the majority will only continue to impose a financial burden upon themselves if this is reasonable and if it is given to an increasingly well-run industry.

The State can help in many ways.

If agriculture cannot spend sums on research comparable with those laid out by the larger industrial concerns, then the State should spend generously both in research and in disseminating knowledge as it is acquired. Again, if other industries are to be offered protection against unfair competition, no less must be offered to agriculture. Indeed, since farming decisions as to production must be made often far in advance of the event, there is an additional case for safeguards against sudden short-period falls in prices. A degree of certainty and stability is necessary for successful production in a concern where months elapse between sowing and reaping and where often years pass between conception and maturity in livestock. Then too there should be no sudden reversal of policies; no sudden withdrawal or drastic diminution of present financial help or other safeguards. Actual proposals made must also have regard to things as they are, and not to mere theory.

Nevertheless, it is incontrovertible that the ultimate decision as to what is to be produced must be determined in the widest interests of the nation. We repeat our previous questions. What can British agriculture produce most effectively and most economically having regard to our soil, climate, and economic conditions? What does the consumer need most from British agriculture?

By a fortunate combination of circumstances, the answer to both questions is the same. Recent discoveries all emphasize the importance to human welfare of the part played by the "health-protective" foods as distinct from energy-building foods. These health-protective foods are those which protect people against deficiency diseases and which promote good health and well-being. The main foods falling in this category are milk (pre-eminently), fresh fruit, vegetables and eggs. And for the production of these Britain is specially fitted by natural conditions; and can be still better fitted, in regard to milk, by the application of the new knowledge now available for improving grassland cultivation. Moreover, British farming enjoys a natural protection in these perishable products through proximity to the market.

We are thus led to the view that the major interests of the farmer and the consumer can be simultaneously met; that we can effect a true marriage of agriculture and nutrition.

We are convinced that much greater financial assistance should be given towards the improvement of our livestock. We refuse to be satisfied with a public expenditure of the present meagre £150,000 per annum on the partial investigation of animal diseases when these cause to the nation an annual loss estimated at £19,000,000. Nor can we rest content with a Milk Scheme which, at the expense of the Treasury and the milk-drinking public, is aimed at propping up dairying in those areas where climate or soil make milk production relatively dear, or in expanding butter or cheese making. Neither can we envisage with equanimity a continuingly large subsidy towards creating a bacon industry which must be a processing rather than a farming venture, which must depend so largely upon the price of foreign-grown feeding stuffs and which must challenge a long-established industry in friendly countries whose efficiency we cannot equal because it has been moulded into their dairying in a manner we cannot now copy.

We urge strongly that producer-elected Marketing Boards with statutory powers to fix prices and create monopolies are wrong in principle and have proved to be indefensible in practice.

As regards milk, a reconstituted Board might in time bring about a spectacular increase in consumption to the mutual benefit of the nation's physique and the dairy industry. Milk for children and mothers could be purchased in increasing quantities from the cheap-producing areas. Considerable economies should also be possible in milk distribution. These measures, coupled with our long-range proposals for improving the breeding stock and eradicating the expense of disease, coupled with efficient, supervised pasteurisation, should effect a reduction in the price at present undreamed of. They should be supplemented by a subsidy towards the consumption of milk. With the reduction in price which this would render possible and with suitable education, our national consumption of this most valuable food could be raised to a level compatible with nutritional requirements. The resultant addition, after a term of years, to our national herd of 1 to 2 million extra cows would give livelihood to a large number of men and women.

We suggest a substantial experiment in the public ownership of land (not the public management of farming). We do this not in pursuit of any theory but for the purely practical considerations outlined in the book.

We urge the duty of the community, in turn, to offer the efficient agricultural producer a return and a prospect reasonably comparable with what he might expect in other fields. But the farmer, no more than the industrialist, can expect the State to guarantee his profits.

In a business which can be so markedly affected by world prices as farming, prudence demands the safeguarding of producers against ruin by guaranteeing a bottom price calculated to limit loss, though not framed to guarantee a profit to the average producer. The claim for such an insurance is doubly powerful at a period when world prices fluctuate violently and the future trends are so uncertain.

We should, however, avoid the real danger of agriculture becoming stereotyped, caught in the vice of "schemes" and quotas which aim at the supply of specified quantities of commodities regardless of the march of time, of discovery, of developments in other lands, or of the growing and prior claims of other branches of farming. In a country where mixed farming predominates, it is vital to allow elasticity in management and production. We should rest content with safeguarding farmers against violent fluctuations, but not seek to prevent long-period changes in the relative output of commodities in line with world movements. Changes in method, in the prices of particular articles of food, are inevitable. Any attempt to perpetuate the present arbitrary "balance" between various branches of farming must also mean that the State will be perpetually competing against itself. Every grant to improve the lot of one section of farmers will be followed by political pressure from other sections for a corresponding grant in order to restore the "balance." Every attempt to guarantee a remunerative price for a definite quantity of a commodity creates a vested interest which must inevitably oppose any reduction either in the quantity or the price of the commodity produced.

The dangers and possible political abuses of price fixing and guarantees have been demonstrated by the pressure brought to bear on Parliament to enlarge the maximum acreage and raise the minimum price under the Wheat (Quota) Scheme. As long, too, as farmers feel that Parliament should be responsible for their day-to-day economic welfare, so long will Parliament be blamed for every adversity or bad time.

Finally, we submit that only an agricultural policy which satisfies the tests of quality of product and efficiency of management can be relied upon to survive the increasing budgetary difficulties and probably rising cost of living facing the nation; and that, therefore, only such a policy can offer to the agricultural producer that degree of stability and permanency necessary for his successful operation.

We ask that our views should receive reasoned consideration as non-party disinterested views, arrived at after exhaustive investigation pursued with the object of arriving at the truth. Our primary desire has been not to advocate any particular policy but to awaken public attention to the importance of the issues discussed and to provide material upon which an informed judgment may be based. Granted a reorientation such as we outline, we see a future for agriculture full of hope.

Those who have given us their views or have commented on parts of the draft at various stages include: Mr. C. S. Orwin, Dr. R. McG. Carslaw, Prof. A. W. Ashby, Prof. R. G. Stapledon, Sir William Dampier, Sir John Orr, Dr. J. A. Hanley, Prof. R. G. White, Dr. B. A. Keen, Dr. R. G. Hatton, Mr. S. T. Wright, Mr. A. P. McDougall, Dr. J. Mackintosh, Mr. Robert Scott, Mr. E. M. H. Lloyd, Dr. K. A. H. Murray, Mr. W. H. Senior, Mr. A. J. Hosier, Mr. C. V. Dawe, Mr. Edgar Thomas, Miss Ruth Cohen, Dr. John Orr, Dr. A. G. Ruston, Dr. W. F. Darke, Mr. S. T. Morris, Mr. N. B. Bagenal and Mr. John Keith.

We obtained reports and memoranda on special subjects, i.e., from Mr. H. G. Davidson, on Pigs; Mr. R. P. Askew, on Sheep; Mr. J. H. Smith, on Poultry; Mr. A. P. McDougall, on Livestock Marketing; Dr. W. F. Darke, on Vegetables; Mrs. R. O. Gibson, on the Farm Worker and on Agricultural Credit; and from Messrs. J. Pryse Howell, Edgar Thomas, C. V. Dawe, W. H. Senior, S. T. Morris, W. F. Darke, and Drs. P. Manning and A. G. Ruston, on Smallholdings.

We emphasize that none of the above is responsible for our conclusions.

We received statistical and other material from the Ministry of Agriculture, the Departments for Agriculture for Scotland and for Northern Ireland, the Imperial Economic Committee, the Milk Marketing Boards (England and Wales and Scotland); the Pigs, Bacon, and Bacon Development Boards; the Potato Marketing Board; from the Sugar Commission; the Livestock Commission; the British Oil and Cake Mills, Ltd.; Messrs. Silcocks, Ltd.; the Millers' Mutual Association; from County Land Agents and Smallholdings Officers; County Agricultural Organizers; the Headquarters and Local Branch Secretaries of the National Farmers' Union and of the Agricultural Workers' Union; from the Low Temperature Research Station, Cambridge; the East Malling and Long Ashton Fruit Research Stations; the New Zealand Meat Producers' Board; the Rowett Institute; Imperial Chemical Industries, Ltd.; Fordson Estates, Ltd.; and as regards allotments, the National Allotments Society; the Scottish Union of Allotment Holders; the Friends' Allotments Committee; the Food Canning Council; from Lord Phillimore, Dr. T. Wallace, Messrs. H. M. Conacher, John Edwards, Spencer W. Mount, F. S. Dennis, D. W. Dinsdale, and W. H. Long.

We did not call upon representatives of landowners, of Borough or County Councils, of distributive or processing trades, or the workers or the co-operatives to state their views on questions such as land tenure, distribution, or other matters of policy, where the arguments for or against are well known.

ASTOR

B. SEEBOHM ROWNTREE

CONTENTS

PART ONE

PRELIMINARY SURVEY

CHAPTER   PAGE

I. INTRODUCTORY 31
Emergency Legislation for Agriculture since 1931 —Practical difficulties now arising—Need for Long-term Policy—What Objectives?—What should be the role of Agriculture in Britain?

II. OBJECTIVES OF AGRICULTURAL POLICY . 43
Past Decades of Adversity in Farming—The Claim for a Larger Agriculture—Difficulties in curtailing Food Imports—Sociological Reasons for increasing the Rural Population—Rural Standard of Life—Security in time of War—Food Storage—Fertility of the Soil—Nutrition and Agriculture—Expanding Market for "Protective Foods"—Promotion of Efficiency—Reasonable Stability for Home Producers.

III. THE CHANGING STRUCTURE OF BRITISH AGRICULTURE, 1866-1938 . . . 63
Seventy Years of Change—Rising Standard of Life and Increased Consumption of Health Foods —Growth of the various kinds of Food Imports— Changes in Cropping—Arable gives way to Grass —Modifications in the Rotation—Yields per acre —Increased Cattle Numbers, especially for Dairy-ing—Fewer Sheep but more Grass-fed—Problems of Mixed Farming—Recent Expansion of Pig Industry—Rapid Development of Poultry-keeping —The Gross and Net Output of Agriculture.

PART TWO

CROPS

IV. GRASS 99
The Predominance of Grass—Climate—Distribu-tion of Rough Grazing, Permanent and Temporary Grass—Soil Fertility—Seed Selection—Manuring

CHAPTER   PAGE

*Grassland Regeneration—Rotational Grazing—
Grass Preservation: Silage, Hay-making, Grass-
drying—Other Grassland Crops—State Policy—
Fertilizer Subsidies—Need for more Assistance.*

V. GRAIN CROPS 108
*Crops complementary to Live-stock—Geographi-
cal Distribution of Acreage—Rising Costs of
Production—Economies of Mechanization—Corn
Merchants—Imports—Future Outlook Overseas
—The Wheat Act of 1931—The Act of 1937—
Use and Abuse of a Guaranteed Price—Proposed
Gradual Reduction of Assistance—Retain Price-
insurance.*

VI. ROOTS AND SUGAR POLICY . . . 117
*Varieties of Root Crops—Labour Costs—Decline
in turnips and mangolds—The Sugar-beet Experiment, 1924–34—The State's Long-term Policy
(1935)—Imports and the Price Fall—Protection
of the Refining Industry—Effects on Agriculture
of the Sugar Experiment—The Cost—Alternative
of Future Policy—Proposed Gradual Reduction
of Assistance.*

VII. FEEDING-STUFFS 126
*Importance of Feeding-stuffs—Winter Feed—
Balanced Rations—Total Supplies—Change-over
to Different Feeding-stuffs as Costs of Production
Change—Imports: Trend in Recent Decades—
Wheat Offals, Barley, Maize, Oil-cake—Import
Duties—Role of British Arable Farming—
Emphasis Shifting to Grass.*

VIII. POTATOES AND HOPS 133
*Diseases of Potatoes—First Earlies—Large Price
Fluctuations—Disposal of Surplus—The Marketing Scheme—Control of Imports—Acreage Control—Riddle Regulations—Authorization of Merchants—Advocate Nominated Board—Hop-
growing highly Localized—Marketing Scheme—
Output and Import Quotas—Need Reconstituted
Board.*

IX. OTHER VEGETABLES 139
*Rapid Development, especially in New Areas—
Motor Transport—Small Growers' Difficulties—
Large-scale Vegetable Specialists, Intensive and
Extensive—Vegetables Popular on Mixed Farms,
Numerous Advantages—Marketing Methods: to
Dealers, Commission Agents, Retailers—Producer*

Retailing—Price Fluctuations—Canning—Grading and Packing—National Mark Scheme—Wholesalers and Retailers—Storage Possibilities—Growth of Vegetable Consumption—Price and Length of Season—Imports and Duties—Vegetables a Minor Interest of Agriculture.

X. FRUIT   144
Expansion mainly in Eastern England, Orchard more than Soft Fruit—Planting Material—Soil Surveys—Manuring—Diseases and Pests—Sprays—Weather—Capital Required—Disposal for Jam—Canning—Fruit-juice Manufacture—Cider—Grading and Packing—Storage—Imports: to what extent Competitive—Tariffs—Fruit Consumption—Importance of Length of Season—Enterprise of Fruit Growers—Future for English Apples—Fruit as a "Health Food."

PART THREE

LIVESTOCK PRODUCTS

XI. CATTLE   153
Output of British Meat Industry—Extent of Imports—Prime Beef and Cow Beef—Geographical Distribution—Breeding—Grass Feeding—Yard Feeding—The Feeders' Margin—"On Farm" Sales—Auctions—Sale by Dead-weight—Grading Problems—Farmer-slaughterhouse—Private and Public Abattoirs—Butchers—Import Restrictions—Cattle Subsidy 1934 and 1937—Tariff—Largely Separate Markets for British, Imported and Cow Beef—Importance of Quality—Measures in Scotland and Ireland—Premium Bulls and Licensing of Bulls Act—Need for Further Measures.

XII. SHEEP   163
Lamb Displacing Mutton—Smaller Store Trade in Sheep than in Cattle—Substitution of Grass-fed for Arable-fed Sheep—Feeders' Margin—Marketing Methods—Imports—Quality of British Mutton and Lamb—Breeding Problems—Disease—Price Insurance.

XIII. PIGS   168
Defects in Breeding—Pigs a Subsidiary Enterprise—Housing—Disease—Management—Fattening on Bought Foods—The Pig Cycle—The Market-

*ing Scheme—Import Restrictions—Pigs Board
and Four Contracts (1933–6)—The 1938 Revision
—Northern Ireland—Reasons for Breakdown in
England—The Bacon Board and the Bacon
Development Board—Improvements in Quality—
Place of Pig Industry in British Agriculture.*

XIV. POULTRY 177
*Eggs and Poultry Meat—Expansion—Different
Types of Producer—Breeding—Hatching—Sex
Detection—Table Poultry Production—Housing
the Laying Flock—Feeding—Seasonality of Output—High Yields—Disease—Other Factors affecting Profitableness—Marketing Methods—Proposals for Reform—Packing Stations—Price
Fluctuations and Storage Possibilities—Imports
—Prospects of Increasing Consumption—Measures
to regulate Breeding and combat Disease—Policy
regarding Marketing and Imports.*

XV. MILK PRODUCTION . . . 186
*Central Importance of Milk—Eastern Arable
and Western Grassland Producers—Length of
Life of the Cow—Milk Yields and Cost per
Gallon—Diseases—Tested Herds and Accredited
Producers—Scales of Premiums—The Hosier
System—Lines of Future Policy.*

XVI. MILK MARKETING 195
*Liquid and Manufacturing Prices before 1914—
The "Platform" Market—Collective Bargaining,
1922–32—The "Basic Surplus" Principle and the
"Declared Quantity"—The Scottish Milk Agency
—Collapse of Manufacturing Prices—The
Marketing Schemes—Fixing Liquid Prices—The
Pool Price System—The Scottish Boards—
Northern Ireland: Prices based on Quality—
Results of the English Scheme—Increased Off-
farm Sales, especially in the West—The Manu-
facturing Market—State Policy for Manufactur-
ing Milk: Price Insurance Plan (1938)—Outlook
for Liquid Consumption—Cream, Skim Milk—
Price Reduction Experiments: Distressed Areas
and Milk in Schools Scheme—Reconstitution of
the Boards—Distribution Problems—Transport
to Town and Depot—Pasteurization and Bottling
—Retailing: Redundancy of Distributors—De-
control Retail Price—Experiments in Distribution
by Local Authorities—Extension of Cheap Milk
Schemes.*

PART FOUR

PERSONNEL AND ORGANIZATION

XVII. THE AGRICULTURAL WORKER . . 211
*The Rural Exodus—Ups and Downs of Trade—
Geographical Differences—Relative Decline in
Numbers of Young Workers—Women and Casual
Labourers—Skill and Training—Wages—Regional
Differences—Overtime—"Special Classes"—En-
forcement—Cost of Living—Food, Clothes—
Housing and Water Supply—The Tied Cottage
—Schools—The Rural Services—Trade Unions
—County Wages Committees—Unemployment
Insurance—Policy for Housing, Water, Education
—Gradual Transformation of Rural Life.*

XVIII. SMALLHOLDERS 219
*A Social Problem—Review of State Activity—
Special Investigations Made—Part-time Holdings
—Full Time: to Provide Independence and Rungs
of a Ladder—Small Market Gardeners versus
Large-scale Growers—Rent, Capital, Equipment,
Secondary Enterprises—Poultry-keeping: Advan-
tage of Large Flock and Diversity of Enterprise
—Growing Risks of Disease—Small Dairymen
more Successful—Future of Producer-Retailers
—Mixed Arable Holdings—Mixed Pasture Hold-
ings—Holder's Previous Occupation—Equipment
of Holding—The Demand and its Satisfaction.*

XIX. FARMERS 230
*Heterogeneity—Farmer, Family Farmer and Small-
holder—Size of Typical Enterprise and Labour
Employed—Farms Changing Hands—Qualities of
a Farmer—A Specimen Budget—Account-keeping
—Skill and Foresight in Buying and Selling—
Management of Resources—Relations with
Workers—No Captains of Agriculture as of
Industry—Obstacles to Changes in Farm Sizes
—The Pros and Cons of Larger Units—Turn to
Subsidiary Businesses—Little Promotion—Need
Experiments in Large-scale Farming—Drastic
Re-organization Impracticable.*

XX. AGRICULTURAL CREDIT 239
*Subject of Constant Complaint—Land Improve-
ment Company—The Banks—Scotland and Ireland—Co-operative Credit Societies and the 1923
Act—The 1928 Act; Agricultural Mortgage Corporation—The "Agricultural Charge" and Regis-*

CHAPTER   PAGE

             tration—Merchant Credit and Proposals for
             Re-organizing it—Co-operative Trading Societies
             —Other Proposals—Adequate Mechanism for
             Supply of Short-term Credit—Long-term Invest-
             ment.

  XXI.   LANDLORDS   243
             Lack of Information—The Landlord's Economic
             Function—Emergence of Non-agricultural Land-
             lords—Course of Rents—Estate Maintenance—
             Death Duties—Experimental Work Transferred
             to Research Stations—Growth of Occupying
             Ownership—Improvements and the Development
             of Tenant Right—The Agricultural Holdings
             Acts—Certificates of Bad Husbandry—Rent Arbi-
             trations—Depletion of Long-term Capital—The
             State's Remedial Policies—Arguments for
             National Ownership—Practical Objections—Pay-
             ing Death Duties with Land—Advocate Land
             Improvement Commissions—Flexible and Gradual
             —Provide for the Maintenance and Development
             of the Fixed Capital in Agriculture.

 XXII.   RESEARCH, EDUCATION AND ADVICE   .   251
             The Second Agricultural Revolution and the
             New Technique—Plant Breeding—Machinery—
             Chemistry—Agro-biology—Fantastic Prospects
             Growth of Research in Britain—State Assistance
             —Plant and Animal Breeding—Animal nutrition
             —Diseases—Mechanization and Electricity—
             Future Policy—Scope of Education—Advisory
             Centres—County Organizers—Farm Institutes
             —Scholarships—Re-organization Needed—Agri-
             cultural Statistics.

                        PART FIVE
                    CONCLUSIONS

XXIII.   CONCLUSIONS   265
             Proposals summarized—National Policy of Im-
             proved Nutrition—Reconstitution of Marketing
             Boards—Acquisition of Agricultural Land through
             Land Improvement Commissions—Measures to
             Promote Efficiency—Revision of Existing Meas-
             ures of Assistance—Need for Caution in this
             Revision—Agriculture not at present unduly
             favoured—Complexity of Agricultural Economic
             Problems.

PART ONE

PRELIMINARY SURVEY

CHAPTER I

INTRODUCTORY

THERE is, we believe, no economic problem to-day to which it is more important that sustained and systematic thought should be directed than that of agricultural policy. Until 1931 the treatment of agriculture by the State was governed by the acceptance of Free Trade and *laissez-faire* as the guiding principles of our commercial policy. The extent of our agriculture as a whole, and the proportions in which it was directed to wheat, meat, milk, vegetables or other products, were determined by individual farmers in the light of their judgment of the course of prices; and in the case of many agricultural products, the determining factor in the course of prices was the relative abundance of supplies from overseas. From time to time the State attempted to make conditions easier for farmers by such minor measures as de-rating. In the case of beet sugar, it sought, after the Great War, to stimulate the production of a particular commodity by heavy subsidies. But this was a quite exceptional proceeding. For the most part the State stood outside the agricultural system and left the lines of its evolution to be determined by the free play of economic forces.

After 1931 the position was transformed. The principle of Free Trade was abandoned; and the way was thus opened for the adoption of any measures of protection that might seem expedient. At the same time there was so catastrophic a fall in world agricultural prices that one branch of agriculture after another was plunged in the most serious difficulties, and presented an urgent claim for prompt and effective help. Measures of assistance were duly introduced; and their combined effect was sufficient to avert the menace of financial ruin and to enable the majority of British farmers to earn a reasonable income at a time when acute and widespread distress prevailed among agriculturists in the greater part of the world. But, as was natural in view of the different circumstances of the different problems, the type of assistance given varied greatly from case to case. Some branches of agriculture were assisted by tariffs; some by subsidies; in the case of wheat the principles of duties and subsidies were ingeniously combined; in some cases recourse was had to quota schemes designed to raise prices by restricting the volume of imports; while in others the main reliance was placed on marketing schemes equipped with statutory authority to fix minimum prices.

It is not surprising that an agricultural policy which has evolved in this way and which consists of measures so heterogeneous in character, improvised to meet a succession of particular emergencies, and uninformed by any general principle, should contain many anomalies and give rise to many serious problems. It was more or less inevitable that some of the more complex of the new expedients adopted should encounter unexpected difficulties. It was inevitable that some branches of agriculture should experience a greater benefit than others from the intervention of the State; and only natural that the less-favoured branches should come to regard the benefits obtained by others as a justification for demanding more assistance for themselves. It was inevitable that the protection accorded to British agriculture should affect the interests of the countries from which we obtain our agricultural imports, and which in turn purchase the products of our manufacturing industries; and only natural therefore that it should raise serious issues of high commercial policy, in which our exporting industries are vitally concerned. Such questions seemed to matter comparatively little during the period of emergency. The immediate need then was to avert the possibility of something like a collapse of British agriculture. By what precise means this could best be accomplished was of secondary importance; the wider repercussions of the measures adopted could be considered when they revealed themselves.

But seven years have now passed since the autumn of 1931, and with each succeeding year the anomalies and the disadvantages entailed by our present makeshift arrangements become increasingly apparent. The farmers are far from satisfied with what has been done on their behalf and continually press, with the backing of some influential opinion, for further measures of assistance. On the other hand the measures already taken are arousing a growing volume of public criticism and discontent. This criticism is levelled partly at the effects of agricultural protection on the cost of living, partly at its effects on international trade, and partly at the burden which agricultural subsidies impose on the national finances. The trend of underlying circumstances is steadily increasing the practical force which attaches to the objections under each of these headings.

So long as the general movement of prices was downward and the cost of living was thus tending to fall, tariffs or restrictions could be imposed on food imports without arousing serious opposition from the consuming public. It could, of course, be argued against these measures that the cost of living would have fallen still more if they had not been imposed; but criticism of this type falls on deaf ears. It is otherwise when the cost of living shows a marked tendency to rise. There is then a disposition to attach an exaggerated share of the blame to any factor which obviously tends to make the cost of living higher than it otherwise would be. Let us suppose, for example, that retail food prices are rising not because of any increase in the prices received by the farmers, but owing to an increase in the distributor's margin, and that this in turn is due to higher wages for the work people in the distributive trades or to a rise in transport costs. The public, in such circumstances, will view measures of agricultural protections, which help to keep food prices high, with increasing disfavour. This became evident in 1937 when the cost of living began to increase sharply. For the time being this tendency has been checked by the setback in the world prices of primary products which occurred in the autumn of that year. But having regard to the world economic situation and in particular to the effects which the rearmament programme must be expected to exert, it seems probable that the prevailing tendency in Great Britain for some years to come will be for the cost of living to move upwards, though it by no means follows that the movement will entail better profit margins for farmers. If so, the cost of living will remain a matter of sufficient political importance to make it difficult for any government to take further steps to assist agriculture at the expense of the consuming public.

Nor is it likely to be much easier in practice to give further assistance in the form of subsidies. The subsidies which have been given in recent years were given when Budgetary conditions were unusually easy. Following the crisis of 1931, the condition of the national finances steadily improved, and Budget surpluses and tax remissions became the order of the day. So long as these conditions remained it was possible to grant financial assistance to agriculture from the Exchequer without imposing palpable burdens on the taxpayer. The necessity to rearm has, however, transformed the financial outlook. Taxation is now again on the increase; even so, the State is unable to defray the whole of its expenditure out of current revenue; a large sum is to be met during the next few years by loans which will necessarily entail continuing charges on the Budget; and it would not be surprising if the rearmament programme costs considerably more than has been estimated before it is complete. In these circumstances, Chancellors of the Exchequer must be expected to subject proposals for further agricultural subsidies to an increasingly sour scrutiny and, perhaps, to turn an inquisitive eye on some of the existing subsidies, e.g. those for sugar beet or fat cattle, which together cost the Exchequer over £10 millions a year.

Recent developments have also served to increase the importance attached to broad considerations of the maintenance and recovery of international trade. For some years after the abandonment of the Free Trade principle in 1931, most people paid little heed to the repercussions that measures of domestic protection might exert on British exports, and still less to their repercussions on international trade in general. It was obvious that the old Free Trade dogma, that imports are paid for by exports, was far from exact; since a tendency for imports to increase while exports declined, with the consequent development of a seriously adverse balance of payments, was an underlying factor in the crisis of 1931 which led to the enforced departure of Great Britain from the gold standard. There seemed no fundamental reason, therefore, why imports might not be reduced without a corresponding decline of exports; indeed to achieve precisely this, or in other words, to redress the adverse balance of trade, and thus restore confidence in sterling, was for some time the main objective of our economic policy. As for the effects of British policy on the interests of other countries, this was not a matter to which the Government could be expected to pay careful regard. The attention of other countries was concentrated also on their own internal problems. Each country took steps which it hoped might be favourable to its own recovery, with small regard to their international repercussions.

Gradually, however, the position has undergone a profound change. From the economic standpoint it has become clear that though imports and exports need not exactly balance, they can diverge only to the extent to which international lending or borrowing takes place, and that the relationship between them is essentially reciprocal. This relationship has been emphasized by the trade agreements which have been made between many different countries in recent years. The British trade agreements have been mainly with agricultural countries overseas; and their broad effect is to safeguard these countries against the danger of further restrictions on their sales to the British market in return for concessions of material benefit to British exporting industries. Export trade remains so important an element in British economic life as to make it extremely improbable that any government would be willing to reverse the policy which these agreements embody. It has become clear, moreover, that other British interests, besides those of the exporting industries, are bound up with the maintenance of close and friendly relations with the agricultural countries over seas. These countries include the British Dominions, whose interests we are bound to treat in a considerate manner. They include South American countries, in the development of which large sums of British capital have been invested. They include the Scandinavian countries, so akin to us in race, political tradition, institutions and ideas, which are coming to occupy the position of outposts of constitutional government in a totalitarian Europe. They include the United States.

Thus broad economic and high political considerations combine, with the growing self-consciousness of the consuming public, to bar the road to further large extensions of agricultural protection. Indeed, to put the point in this negative form is to understate it. There is a widespread desire in the majority of democratic countries for a new attempt to secure a reduction of trade barriers, partly for its own sake, and partly in the hope that it would facilitate political appeasement. The welcome accorded to the project of a trade agreement between Great Britain and the United States is one indication of the strength of this desire. The mission entrusted to M. van Zeeland, which led to his Report with its proposals for a Pact of economic collaboration, forms another. Indeed, the promotion of greater economic co-operation between nations has come to be widely regarded as an essential objective of a wise international policy. There are, it is true, many difficulties in the way which are likely to make progress in this direction slow and halting at the best. But it is the hope of almost everyone who feels concern for the future of international relations that the attitude of the British Government will prove helpful rather than obstructive.

Nothing could be more unfortunate, nothing in the long run would be more prejudicial to the interests of farmers, than the development of a situation in which their sectional interests were placed in sharp conflict with both the material interests of the community as a whole, and the central objectives of national policy. Yet there is some danger, as matters are now drifting, that such a conflict may arise. Having suffered for generations from the dominance of the Free Trade philosophy, farmers are instinctively averse to aspirations for an increase in the flow of international trade. Having long been denied any protection against overseas competition in the name of the consumer, they regard with frank hostility all talk about the importance of cheap food. They are conscious that on several occasions in recent years they have succeeded in extorting concessions from governments by political pressure, and they fail perhaps to appreciate how much the effectiveness of their pressure depended on a favourable tide of national sentiment. Moreover, as has already been indicated, they are far from satisfied with the existing position. It is true that most branches of farming have been fairly prosperous in the last two or three years; but these have been years of general economic recovery, in which most industries have made good profits. Not all sections of farmers have shared in the general prosperity, while almost all have experienced new difficulties, notably an increasing scarcity of agricultural labour which gives them grounds for anxiety as to the future. If agriculture is to retain, against the competition of urban employment, an adequate supply of efficient labour, it is evident that agricultural wages will have to be raised steadily and substantially. Thus the future outlook for farmers, should world agricultural prices again take an unfavourable turn, is by no means secure even on the basis of the present arrangements. The "scissors" action of falling prices and rising costs, through which they have suffered so severely in the past, may at any time reassert itself.

With this psychology and with these anxieties the farmers are disposed to put their claims for Government assistance high, while the Government, for the reasons already indicated, must feel it increasingly difficult to satisfy them. As a result, the evolution of agricultural policy appears to have passed for the time being into a phase of deadlock in which problems requiring action accumulate unsolved. It may well be that this phase of deadlock will continue for a considerable time. None the less, it has become, we think, urgently necessary that the principles which should guide our agricultural policy should be systematically considered. It ought to be possible to formulate the broad lines of an agricultural policy which will be just to the farming community, acceptable to public opinion as a whole, appropriate to the changing conditions of the present day and harmonious with national policy in wider spheres. To contribute to this task is the object of the present book.

Before, however, detailed issues of agricultural policy can usefully be discussed, it is necessary to consider first the objectives which that policy should pursue. How far should we aim at enlarging the volume of British agricultural production ? How far is it wise to attempt to grow at home part of the food we now import from overseas ? Clearly there must be limits to such a policy. How are those limits to be defined ? On what principles are they to be based ? Hitherto these questions have been left virtually in abeyance; but they are questions to which before long it will be imperative to formulate an answer.

But that is not all. What are the types of British agriculture whose expansion it would be most desirable to promote ? Should we concentrate mainly on assisting those branches of agriculture, such as wheat, which have declined most seriously in recent generations and which find it hardest to hold their own in competition with overseas producers? Or should we rather aim at promoting the development of those branches of agriculture for which we are relatively well suited by virtue of geographical and climatic conditions? Should we strive, in other words, to revive the agriculture of the past or look to the development of a new agriculture for the future? This again is a question which has hardly, as yet, received serious consideration. The general tendency of the emergency measures of assistance improvised during the last few years has indeed been to favour most those branches of agriculture for which we appear on the whole to be relatively ill suited. This was only natural in the circumstances and indicates no deliberate choice of principle. But there is some danger lest we should find ourselves committed by these improvisations to a choice of principle which is the opposite to that which we should have made if we had faced the question clearly on its merits.

Behind these questions there lies another more fundamental still. What sort of role is it that agriculture should properly play in our national life? Should agriculture be regarded as one industry or one group of industries among others existing primarily for the purpose of producing commodities to satisfy the public wants? Or is it to be regarded as something essentially distinct from industry as a separate way of life with a special value of its own, as a vital element in the social structure, as a reservoir of national vitality and strength? Under the influence of the Free Trade tradition British agricultural policy has hitherto been based in effect on the former conception. But in many countries on the continent the other conception prevails, and in this country too it makes a wide appeal. This is a question which may not admit of a clear-cut decided answer in the one sense or the other. None the less, it urgently needs dispassionate consideration. For the view which a man takes upon this question, however vague or incoherent it may be, goes far to determine his approach to the concrete questions of agricultural policy.

We repeat that the serious consideration of these questions has as yet hardly begun. So long as the Free Trade régime prevailed they did not arise. Subsequently, the pressure of emergency problems served for a time to keep them in the background. But they are questions which can no longer be ignored. It is idle to imagine that the necessity for answering them can be removed by a return to the principle of *laisser-faire*, by re-establishing the free play of economic forces in an environment either of Free Trade or of a low uniform level of agricultural import duties, as the determinant of our agricultural system. Particular control schemes which encounter difficulties may be modified or abandoned. The treatment that we accord to agricultural imports may be altered in the direction of greater simplicity and uniformity. But there will certainly be no return to the old conditions under which the prosperity or adversity of the different branches of agriculture was regarded as lying outside the proper functions of the State. In the sphere of agricultural economics, at least, the dethronement of *laisser-faire* is final, and there is no real possibility of a restoration. For the fundamental economic conditions which made *laisser-faire* a workable principle in the nineteenth century have passed away. When the populations of European countries were increasing with immense rapidity, the chief need was for a constant expansion of productive capacity in every branch of economic life, for the erection of new factories in industry, for the opening up of new areas of agricultural production. So long as that was the chief need, the advantages of *laisser-faire* were great, its disadvantages comparatively unimportant. By giving free scope to the initiative of enterprising individuals, it secured a more rapid expansion of productive capacity than it would have been easy to effect by any scheme of governmental planning. The expansion might at times be misdirected; a temporary surplus of productive capacity might reveal itself here or there, with the attendant consequences of unremunerative prices and business losses. But so long as the trend of numbers was strongly upwards, these difficulties were sure to prove short-lived. Nowadays, when there is a widespread tendency for populations to become stabilized or even in some cases to show prospects of decline, the situation is different. A surplus of productive capacity in particular directions may reveal itself not as a transient but as a persistent phenomenon; and this may entail widespread disaster for producers if they are left to face the situation under conditions of unregulated competition. Largely for this reason there has been a movement from *laisser-faire* towards regulation and control in all branches of economic life.

In agriculture the consequences of a condition of persistent over-production are especially formidable. Most industrial commodities are only produced in response to definite orders, and, however bad trade may be, manufacturers will not quote at prices which entail a decided loss. But the farmer must decide the scale of his output in advance of any contract for sale; and he must subsequently dispose of his produce at whatever prices he is able to obtain. If when this time arrives demand falls seriously short of supply, prices may be forced down to levels which are ruinous even to the most efficient agriculturists working under the most favourable natural conditions.

This, or something very like it, was what happened to world agriculture in 1931 and the immediately succeeding years. Agricultural communities throughout a large part of the world were plunged into extreme distress; and almost every Government felt compelled to improvise ʃspecial expedients for the assistance of its agriculturists. We do not believe that it would have been practicable under these conditions for any British Government to have left our farmers to their fate. Such a course could not have been followed without the danger of ruining many of our most enterprising and efficient farmers and of inflicting lasting damage to British agricultural life. If this be true of the past the moral for the future is inescapable. For the reasons indicated there can be no assurance that another crisis of world agricultural over-production may not occur, and we cannot afford to re-establish conditions which would expose our agriculture in such an eventuality to the risk of avoidable disaster.

But if the abandonment of *laisser-faire* must thus be accepted as final, what new policy is to be put in the vacant place ? Are we to be content with safeguarding agriculture against the new menace to its stability which arises from the altered conditions of the modern world ? Should we, on the other hand, use the opportunity to pursue larger and more positive aims ? This question even in its broadest aspects is, as we have already seen, one of great complexity. We shall devote our next chapter to an attempt to answer it.

CHAPTER II

OBJECTIVES OF AGRICULTURAL POLICY

THOUGH there was no world agricultural depression before the Great War of comparable severity to that of the last few years, British farmers suffered seriously from time to time from the unrestricted competition of imports from overseas. Indeed, the view was widely held at the time, and has since received a still wider measure of support, that the interests of agriculture were unduly sacrificed in the nineteenth century to those of industrial development. Certainly the consequences entailed by the agricultural depression of the 'eighties and 'nineties were serious and far-reaching. It was not merely that certain types of agriculture such as wheat-production declined seriously or that the townward drift of the rural population was accentuated. The long-continued adversity left an enduring mark on the spirit and outlook of British farmers, and sapped the enterprise which many of them had previously displayed. Mr. R. C. K. Ensor in his *England:* 1870-1914, paints the following picture:

"Down to 1880, despite all the marvellous expansion of mining and manufacture and metallurgy, agriculture retained a kind of headship. It employed incomparably more people than any other single industry. With its fortunes those of the rest still largely fluctuated; a good harvest quickened trade all round, a bad one slowed it. More than a century of keen practical research and experiment, for which nobility and even royalty shared the credit with commoners, had lifted its technology far ahead of most farming on the continent. Its breeds were the best, its cropping the most scientific, its yields the highest; its virtually universal substitution of horses for oxen for all purposes of farm traction typified visibly its specialization for quality and its application of superior force. Its wages, though low to our eyes, were the highest agricultural wages in Europe and represented a distinctly better standard of material comfort than that of most of the self-employed peasantry in similar European latitudes. Much the same may be said of its housing conditions. Its worst remaining employment abuse— the gang system—had been finally exposed and practically suppressed in the 'sixties. Joseph Arch's agricultural trade-union movement, launched in February 1872, and prudently conducted by dissenting preachers, succeeded in raising wages over wide areas by 1s. 6d. or 2s. a week, and in some cases by 3s. or 4s., besides improving hours and conditions. It suffered a defeat in 1874, but would probably have recovered itself, had not the beginnings of the depression followed in 1875. After 1877, when tens of thousands of workers were discarded yearly, wages fell by as much as they had previously risen, and more. Farmers themselves sank into ever increasing embarrassment— bankruptcies and auctions followed each other; the country-side lost its most respected figures. Those whose pride in, and conscience towards, the land was greatest, suffered most; for the only chance of survival was to lower farming standards all round. Across the stricken field strange birds of prey flitted; speculators who bought populous cornlands for conversion into uninhabited sheep-runs; or 'pirate' tenants, who went from one farm to another exhausting the soil by a policy of taking without giving. Adjustments, as time went on, were made; but always upon the basis of withdrawing both capital and men from the land. For twenty years the only chance for any young or enterprising person on the countryside was to get out of it. The motto over the door of Dante's *Inferno* might have been truthfully posted at the entrance of a typical English village.

So was consummated the urbanizing of a nation, which till a century before had possessed only one great city, and whose traditions of popular culture were almost entirely rural."[1]

The colours of this picture may be darker than the facts justify, as indeed our next chapter will suggest. But the passage well describes the demoralizing influence which naked exposure to overseas competition exerted on some branches of British agriculture. As we argued in the last chapter, the consequences of such exposure might be far

[1] R. C. K. Ensor, *England:* 1870–1914, pp. 117–18. (London, Humphrey Milford, 1936).

more serious under the conditions likely to prevail in future. It is fairly easy for a country which imports a large proportion of its food supplies to ensure a reasonable stability of prices for its home producers at a comparatively small cost to its consuming public. To go thus far at any rate is in our view essential.

But there are many who would go much further, and who insist that it is not enough to safeguard the economic prosperity of British agriculture on its present shrunken scale, but that the opportunity should be taken to repair the neglect of the past, to diminish our dependence on imported food-stuffs, and to increase once more the part which agriculture plays in our national life. This is the first large issue upon which it is important that we should clear our minds.

A policy which attempted to find room for a large expansion of our present agricultural production by curtailing imports from overseas would be exposed to very serious objections. It would either entail heavy subsidies, and a consequent increase in taxation; or it must make food more expensive than it would otherwise be for the consuming public. In either case, it must tend to impoverish the community as a whole. It would prejudice the interests of the exporting industries. It might endanger our good relations with the countries from which we have been accustomed to import food on a large scale and the good-will of which may be of value to us in time of war.

In the preceding chapter, we have seen that the drift of events is tending to increase the practical force of these various objections. But the question is not one that can be settled on the basis of momentary currents of political expediency. We have to consider dispassionately how much weight properly attaches to the objections we have enumerated, as against the advantages that can be urged on the other side.

For this purpose it is desirable, we think, in the first instance to approach the question in a wide perspective. The fundamental argument on which the Free Trade philosophy of the nineteenth century was based was that international trade gave rise to an international division of labour under which different countries concentrated on those kinds of economic activity for which each was relatively best suited. By specializing in this way and by exchanging their products with one another, they derived, it was claimed, a great mutual benefit, analogous to that which comes within any country from the specialization of its citizens on different tasks. This was the argument which received its classic expression in Adam Smith's *Wealth of Nations*. In Victorian Britain it was accepted as a truth that had been triumphantly demonstrated by events; and the reason why it was so accepted was the manifest character of the advantages attaching to the exchange of the manufactured goods of industrial countries for the primary products of agricultural communities. It was here that the benefits of international trade were indisputable and conspicuous. It would have clearly been impossible for Great Britain to have maintained a rapidly multiplying population while steadily improving the standard of life, if she had relied on her own agricultural resources. It was indeed only because of the development of international trade along lines which entailed a large and growing importation of food and raw materials from overseas that the gloomy predictions made by Malthus at the end of the eighteenth century were falsified. The advantages to the agricultural communities were no less clear. These were largely new countries, with undeveloped resources. International trade, combined with international investment, enabled them to build railways, to erect towns, to sink mines, to maintain a rate of economic development which would have been impossible, if they had to rely on their own savings and their own industrial capacity.

The development of an international division of labour between the old world and the new, between industrial and agricultural communities, was thus in its essential features a highly beneficial process. Indeed, Great Britain's rapid economic progress in the nineteenth century was largely due to the leading part which she took in it. It is possible, of course, to maintain that it would have been better in the long run if this development had proceeded somewhat more slowly. It may even be argued that it would have been better if it had proceeded less far. It might conceivably have been better, even under the conditions of the nineteenth century, if the development of international trade had been subject to such measures of control as would have maintained the prosperity of British agriculture, even though they had retarded somewhat the general rate of economic progress. The question is a complex one; and it is needless now to consider whether such measures would have been wise or practicable. In fact, for good or ill, the expansion of international trade was allowed to proceed with an uncontrolled momentum. As a result, a large agricultural productive capacity has been developed in the United States, in South America, in Scandinavia and in the British Dominions for the supply of the British market. It is indeed of the essence of the present world agricultural problem that this productive capacity has become in respect of many staple commodities in excess of the requirements of the market; and owing to the altered trend of Western populations this excess of agricultural productive capacity may well prove a persistent or at least a frequently recurrent phenomenon. This, as we have already seen, is the main reason for fearing that world agricultural prices may in future undergo prolonged periods of depression, and it supplies a strong argument for measures designed to protect British agriculture against the vicissitudes of world prices.

But the same consideration supplies an equally strong argument against making it our aim to reduce our imports of food in order to make room for a larger output of British agricultural produce. From the standpoint of a rational development of the world's economy, such a policy would involve a glaring paradox. It would mean setting out to enlarge our own agricultural production at a time when there is a clearly marked tendency towards a surplus of productive capacity in the world as a whole. This would be to aggravate one of the most difficult of the economic problems by which the modern world is confronted. It is true that other European countries have taken precisely this course; the development of an extreme agrarian protectionism over a large part of Europe has indeed been a major factor in aggravating the difficulties of the agricultural exporting countries in recent years. But the strength and prosperity of Great Britain in the past have been largely based on the development of extensive and harmonious trade relations with the outside world. Great Britain is herself the centre of an Empire which consists in the main of agricultural exporting communities depending largely for their prosperity upon the British market. In this position and with these traditions, Great Britain cannot prudently afford to pursue a policy which disregards the vital economic interests of friendly agricultural communities, or which would be incompatible with the basic requirements of the international economic situation.

When we turn to the detailed facts of British agriculture, the effect of these broad considerations is greatly reinforced. When we turn in later chapters to consider the problems of the different sections of farming, we shall find that two facts force themselves repeatedly on our attention. The first is that the products of British agriculture often differ materially in kind or quality from the imported commodities which bear the same name, and in an important degree are bought by different classes of consumers or are used for different purposes. British beef, for example, includes a certain quantity of the highest quality, which commands a specially high price and which meets what may be regarded as a luxury demand. On the other hand, much British beef is of poor quality, and would not readily be accepted by the consuming public as a satisfactory substitute for imported beef. British bacon is of varying quality and differs from Danish bacon. British wheat is a very different commodity from Canadian wheat, and is mainly used, not as it is natural to suppose for bread, but for biscuits.

These differences of quality and function have an important bearing on the problems of agricultural protection. For it is not as easy as it would be if the products were identical, to secure a larger demand for British agricultural products by restricting imports from overseas. As we shall see later for example, the restrictions imposed on imports of bacon have been followed by a rise in the price of imported bacon relatively to that of British bacon. They have only been partially successful in diverting the demand for bacon from the imported to the British variety; to some extent they have led to a smaller consumption of bacon. In so far as this has happened the consuming public has suffered an injury without any compensating benefit to British agriculture. Considerations of this kind apply to a wide range of agricultural commodities.

The second point which emerges from a study of British agriculture is that the finished product of one section of agriculture is often, to employ a common phrase, the raw material of another. We shall see later that the cereals grown in Great Britain are used mainly as the food not of human beings but of animals. They represent, that is to say, part of the raw material of the live-stock industry. In its turn the live-stock industry includes distinct breeding and fattening sections. It follows that the same protective measures which might be to the advantage of one branch of British farming would often be to the disadvantage of another.

British farming, in short, like British economic life as a whole, has evolved on lines which assume the continuance of large scale imports of agricultural products.

We see, therefore, that against the idea of attempting to enlarge our domestic agricultural production by curtailing food imports from overseas, there are arrayed both grave objections of high economic statesmanship, and formidable practical difficulties. It is with these considerations in mind that we must approach the question of the role which agriculture should properly play in our national life. How far is it right and reasonable that our treatment of agriculture should be influenced by considerations of the type to which we briefly alluded in the previous chapter, such as the special value of agriculture as a corrective of the defects or morbidities of urban civilization?

It is often argued that the fact that only a very small proportion of our population is now employed in agriculture indicates an unnatural state of things, a dangerously "top-heavy" social structure. But it is inevitable that in the ordinary course of human progress the proportion of the population engaged in agriculture will steadily decline. Agriculture is largely concerned with the satisfaction of the elementary wants of man. In a primitive phase of society the greater part of man's energies are necessarily devoted to the satisfaction of these elementary wants, and the majority of people accordingly are to be found engaged in agricultural pursuits. But as man's power over nature increases, he is able to obtain the bare necessities of life with a smaller expenditure of energy, and he is able accordingly to turn more of his attention to the satisfaction of less urgent and more complex wants. As specialization proceeds, this means that a larger proportion of people are withdrawn from agriculture and engage in commercial or industrial pursuits. A decline in the proportion of the population engaged in agriculture is thus an inevitable concomitant of economic progress and an improving standard of life; and it is impossible to lay down, on *a priori* grounds, any limits to the extent to which this proportion may eventually decline. It is true that the proportion of the population engaged in agriculture is far smaller in Great Britain than in any other country, but it is also true that the proportion in other countries is far smaller than it used to be. It is impossible, therefore, to attach any clear meaning to the conception of a "natural" proportion between the agricultural and the industrial population. There may be grounds for deploring the rapidity with which the proportion of the agricultural population has declined in Great Britain; but the arguments to this effect must be justified on their merits. They cannot be fortified by any general appeal to what is natural.

Many detailed arguments are of course frequently advanced in support of this contention. It is urged that agricultural life is physically healthier than industrial life, and that in many respects it is mentally and spiritually healthier as well. The man whose daily work brings him in close contact with the processes of nature will appreciate certain truths that are apt to escape the clerk or the industrial artisan. He will be, in some respects at least, a wiser man. Something of these advantages will extend to the children who are brought up in an agricultural atmosphere, even if they themselves follow urban pursuits. The existence of a substantial agricultural population thus helps to ensure that a still larger proportion of the population have some contact or connection with country life, and this contributes to a sane and balanced outlook from the community as a whole.

In considering these claims it is important to bear two points in mind. In the first place we must distinguish between employment in agriculture and contact with the countryside. That so large a proportion of the population should be concentrated in large towns as is the case in Great Britain to-day is undesirable from many points of view. But it is not inevitable that industrialization should entail this consequence. Nor is it inevitable that the town-dweller should be so effectually cut off from knowledge of the countryside as was the case in the last century. The motor-bus, the motor-cycle and the motor-car are indeed rapidly increasing the rural contacts of the town-dweller at the present time, while there are other technical developments which may encourage a decentralization of industry which will place an increasing number of industrial workers in rural surroundings. Indeed, the proportion of the British population engaged in non-agricultural pursuits is already so overwhelmingly large that it must necessarily be to developments of this type rather than to an extension of agriculture that we must look for a correction of the over-urbanization of our national life.

But the second point is more important for our general

argument. How far agricultural life really possesses the advantages that have been indicated depends in practice on other conditions, notably on the standard of living that agricultural workers are able to obtain. In the actual conditions of contemporary British life, it is very difficult to maintain the claim that the agricultural population taken as a whole is stronger, healthier or wiser than the general mass of the urban community. This is probably true in some parts of the country: it is untrue in others. Doubtless the main reason why it is not more generally true is to be found in the selective character of the process of migration to the towns. For generations past industry has been slowly denuding the countryside of its more vigorous human strains. But so long as there is a marked disparity between the urban and the rural standard of living, this tendency must be expected to continue. Nor is this the whole story. For the rearing of healthy children good nutrition is as important as fresh air; good housing, good drainage and a clean water supply as important as a close contact with nature; and for a prolonged period in many parts of the country the agricultural labourer has been at a serious disadvantage in these respects. It seems to follow that in order to secure the advantages that we are now considering, it is more important to raise the standard of living in agriculture than to increase the numbers of people engaged in it. The choice may be necessary; for it would assuredly not be easy to do both, except at a cost to the rest of the community which in practice would be prohibitive.

There is, of course, an entirely different argument for an enlarged domestic agriculture which is often advanced, and which makes to-day an especially strong appeal, namely, the desirability of diminishing our dependence on imported food with a view to greater security in time of war. It is obvious that in an explosive international atmosphere the safeguarding of our national food supplies in the event of war must be a vital object of national policy. If economic considerations are in conflict with it, they must take second place. If it were true that our safety in time of war would be increased by a policy of high agricultural protection which would diminish our normal importation of foodstuffs, the case for such a policy would be extremely strong; and if this were the speediest and most efficacious method of achieving the desired result the case for it would be overwhelming. In fact, however, we are very doubtful whether high agricultural protection would contribute anything on balance to increase our safety in time of war. Our reasons for this view are set out at some length in our previous volume, *The Agricultural Dilemma*,[1] but in view of the importance of the subject we think it advisable to recapitulate the more important of them here.

In the first place, a policy which succeeded in curtailing materially the volume of our food imports must be expected to cause a corresponding curtailment in the size of our mercantile marine. Our imports are, generally speaking, much bulkier commodities in relation to their value than our exports, so that the volume of British shipping in times of peace depends mainly upon the volume of our import trade. There may at any time, of course, particularly when trade is depressed, be a large reserve of unused ships; but these ships would speedily be broken up if there were no expectation that their services would again be required. If, accordingly, we were to succeed in reducing substantially our normal volume of imports in time of peace, we must reckon with the probability that we should enter upon any war that might occur, with a mercantile marine diminished in proportion.

But that is not all. The size of our ship-building industry is in its turn dependent mainly upon the size of our mercantile marine. If a considerable part of our shipping were to be rendered functionless by a curtailment of food imports, a considerable portion of our shipbuilding yards would similarly become redundant. If this were to happen we could not expect to enter upon a war with an available

[1] Published by P. S. King, London, 1935.

ship-building capacity as large as we now possess. *Personnel* as well as material equipment would, of course, be affected. We should have not only fewer ships and fewer shipyards, but fewer trained seamen and fewer skilled shipwrights. Such would appear to be the almost inevitable consequences of reducing substantially our volume of overseas trade in time of peace.

Now a large mercantile marine, a large ship-building capacity, and a large sea-faring population are vital elements of strength to a naval power like Great Britain. During the last war heavy calls were made upon the resources of the mercantile marine in both material and *personnel* for transporting and maintaining armies overseas, keeping them supplied with munitions, and serving the multifarious needs of the Fleet. It was only because our mercantile marine was large that it was able to meet these calls, and our mercantile marine was large precisely because we were accustomed in times of peace to import immense quantities of food stuffs and raw materials from overseas. Dangerous as our position may have been at the height of the intensive submarine campaign in 1917, it is improbable that our danger would have been less if we had entered upon the war importing say only three-fourths of the commodities we actually did import, but with a mercantile marine only three-fourths as large.

We emphasize this consideration since it is not, we think, sufficiently appreciated in public discussion. We may add that it is no ingenious paradox or superficial technicality. On the contrary its force may, perhaps, be more readily grasped if we state the argument in rather wider and more general terms. Naval power and a large overseas trade are the natural complements of one another. It can be argued that we might be safer in some respects, less vulnerable at least to the danger of starvation, if we were a small nation with a much smaller population, growing all our food at home. But that choice is not open to us. We depend on a large scale flow of imports from overseas, and we cannot escape from this dependence however much we may seek to mitigate it. It follows that our safety in time of war is dependent on naval power, on maintaining the command of the seas and keeping open our trade routes. For this purpose a large overseas trade in time of peace is an asset of the utmost value. A country which aspires to the command of the seas is the last country which can afford to pursue a policy of self-sufficiency.

It is, therefore, we believe, fundamentally false policy to look for security to a reduction of our food imports in time of peace. Our aim should rather be, while maintaining a high volume of imports in peace-time, to take such measures as will enable us to sustain without serious hardship a large curtailment of those imports in time of war. For achieving this aim, we advocate two main lines of action—(1) a well-considered policy of food storage, and (2) measures to maintain and improve the fertility of the soil. The former will give us a reserve of food on which we can draw, the latter will enable us to expand our agricultural production rapidly when the need arises. Such measures would do no damage to our overseas trade in time of peace; they would entail no contraction of our mercantile marine and no injury to our relations with friendly agricultural communities. On the contrary, a storage policy would be of positive benefit to overseas agriculturists, during the phase in which the reserve was being accumulated. Yet such measures would in our opinion be much more efficacious in safeguarding our food-supplies, as well as much more economical, than a policy of increased home production could possibly be.

To appreciate the truth of this contention we must consider the problem in somewhat greater detail. Our most vital food requirement is bread. We rely at present upon imports for about three quarters of our total supply of wheat; these imports come mainly from distant continents, and since wheat is a bulky commodity they require a large amount of tonnage for their transport. Wheat was the chief subject of anxiety as regards food supply in the last war; and it is in respect of wheat that we shall continue to be especially vulnerable.

How much then could a policy of increased peace-time production do to safeguard our wheat supply? We import, as has been said, three-fourths of our annual wheat requirements. This means that our home production amounts only to one-fourth of our requirements, so that if we were to succeed in doubling our home production we should still remain dependent on imports for one-half of our supplies. Yet we imagine that no one acquainted with the facts of British agriculture would regard the doubling of our wheat production as representing a practicable aim. It would be necessary to divert to wheat growing much land which is better suited for other purposes. Huge subsidies, or alternatively, a big rise in the price of bread, would be required; and even so it is doubtful if the objective would be realized.

For ensuring our supplies of wheat, storage is a far more practicable policy. Though many detailed administrative problems necessarily arise, there would be no insuperable difficulty in accumulating in Great Britain a reserve of wheat amounting say to one year's consumption. Such a reserve would contribute as much to the maintenance of our bread supply over a war which lasted for four years as could be achieved by doubling our home production. It would be immeasurably less costly and incidentally it could be accomplished far more economically.

In the case of other important agricultural imports such as meat, bacon and dairy products, rather different considerations arise. An increased home production of these commodities would necessitate increased imports of grain and feeding-stuffs, and although a certain reserve of maize and other feeding-stuffs might be stored, most of the increase in import requirements would have to be set against the diminution in the imports of animal products that would be made possible. Since grain and other feeding-stuffs are bulky commodities, the additional tonnage required to carry them would probably exceed the tonnage that would be saved. In time of war, accordingly, an increase in our home production of meat or bacon would probably do less than nothing to economize shipping space. In the case of bacon this is unquestionably true, as was shown by experience in the last war. It does not follow, however, that an increased production of meat in time of peace might not be of some value from the stand-point of security, if we deliberately pursued a policy of a gradual slaughtering of live-stock when war came. If, in other words, we were to regard our pigs and beef-cattle as little granaries of corn, less vulnerable than ordinary granaries to air attack, they might serve much the same function as food storage. There are limits, however, to the extent to which it would be feasible to treat our live-stock in this way. On the whole, therefore, we may conclude that considerations of security supply some argument, but not a very clear or decisive one, for maintaining live-stock farming on a substantial scale.

In principle, however, there is much to be said for concentrating largely on live-stock production in time of peace, and shifting over to increased cereal production in time of war. This serves to emphasize the importance of the second aim that we have formulated, that of taking measures to improve the fertility of the soil. For this would contribute greatly to our capacity to increase our output of wheat and other essential commodities in time of need. On other grounds indeed, we regard the preservation of the fertility of the soil as an object which deserves the attention of the State. The fertility of the land is perhaps the most important element in the capital resources of British agriculture. Yet it is not an element which it is easy to assess or measure, and it is tempting accordingly for a farmer, under the pressure of unfavourable economic conditions, to make ends meet from year to year by farming methods which in effect exhaust the fertility of the soil. To counteract this temptation should be an important object of public policy.

We return from the issue of security to our broad

argument. Whatever weight may rightly be attached to the various special claims that are advanced on behalf of agriculture, we do not think that there is sufficient force in them to justify an over-riding of our vital national interests in the maintenance of large-scale international trade and in abundant supplies of cheap food for the industrial population. An agricultural policy which is to prove acceptable in the long run to public opinion, must be framed along lines which can be reconciled with these superior needs.

We conclude that it should be no part of British agricultural policy to endeavour to reduce the volume of food imports by tariffs or other protective measures. We must remain true to the principles of an international division of labour on which our national economic life has been built up. This means that wherever agricultural commodities can be produced much more economically abroad than at home, we must remain ready to import them ungrudgingly from overseas. It does not follow that we must leave our farmers altogether without protection against overseas competition. It may be desirable, as we have already suggested, to subject imports to some degree of control in order to ensure to our farmers a reasonable degree of security in the event of a serious depression of world prices. In practice, measures adopted for this purpose may have the incidental effect of stimulating a larger output by British farmers. In so far as this result occurs it would be pedantic to object to it. But the main object of such measures of protection as are adopted must be stability rather than an increase in the volume of home production. This is not an unreal or fine-spun distinction: it is of great practical importance. Wisely chosen measures to ensure a reasonable stability of prices for British farmers might avert disastrous damage to our agricultural life at a slight and imperceptible cost to the consuming public. On the other hand, any attempt to reduce the volume of our food imports permanently by protective means would be likely to entail burdens on the consumers or the taxpayers, altogether disproportionate to the benefits conferred on agriculture.

If this conclusion is accepted, we must recognize that there is not likely to be any large expansion of our domestic production of staple agricultural commodities, such as cereals, meat, butter, and cheese, which we are accustomed to import largely from abroad. For producing these commodities the agricultural communities overseas have many climatic and other natural advantages as compared with British farmers. Moreover, the tendency, which we must expect to continue, towards a raising of the wages and improvement of the conditions of British agricultural labourers is not likely to improve our farmers' competitive position. Here and there it is possible that British farmers may make headway against overseas competition by greater efficiency alike in production and marketing and by improving the quality of the commodities they supply; but in the main it must be expected that we shall continue to import as large a proportion as hitherto of the staple food-stuffs to which we have referred.

In other branches of agriculture, however, the outlook for an expansion of home production is far more hopeful. For many agricultural commodities proximity to the market is a consideration of the first importance. This is notably true of milk. It is hardly less true of most fresh fruits and of vegetables, and it applies in some degrees to eggs and poultry. For producing such commodities British agriculture enjoys, in short, a high degree of natural protection. These, moreover, are commodities for which we may reasonably expect a steadily increasing home demand. They belong to the category of what are known as the "protective foods"[1] as distinct from energy-

[1] Protective foods in general tend to counteract the under-development of the body and the so-called deficiency diseases such as rickets, scurvy, anaemia, goitre and certain forms of defective vision, etc., and other ill-defined conditions of poor health, which often result from diets made up too exclusively of those energy-bearing foods such as cereals, sugar and certain fats which are deficient in important nutritional factors. Protective foods in fact are necessary for the attainment of optimum physical development and health.

building. The present tendency of medical opinion is to emphasize the importance of the health-protective foods to vitality and health, and to urge that they should play a larger part than they now do in the diet of the majority of families. This conjuncture of circumstances offers an obvious opportunity for British farmers, an opportunity which is often expressed in the slogan, "A Marriage of Agriculture and Nutrition."

It seems probable, indeed, that the improvement of the standards of nutrition will come increasingly to be regarded as an important aim of national policy analogous to the improvement of sanitation in the pre-war and of housing standards in the post-war period. Many issues of policy are likely to arise in this connection which it would be outside the scope of this volume to discuss in detail. In general, however, it seems reasonable to assume that the category of the protective foods provides the main scope for the future expansion of British agricultural production.

There are, however, certain obvious conditions that must be fulfilled if this opportunity is to be realized. If we are to secure the steady increase in the consumption of the protective foods that is so desirable, these foods must be clean and good and reasonably cheap. The point of quality and cleanliness is of obvious importance in the case of milk. For long the medical profession has been torn between a general belief in the valuable nutritive qualities of milk and legitimate misgivings as to the quality of much of the milk supplied; and so long as there is room for such misgivings the consumption of the protective foods is unlikely to increase as rapidly as it might otherwise do. For all the protective foods the maintenance of reasonably cheap prices is an essential condition of an adequate expansion of demand. The problem is to reconcile such prices for the consuming public with a reasonable living for the farmers and an improvement in the wages and general conditions of the agricultural population as a whole.

This leads us to a theme which will occur repeatedly

throughout this book—the vital importance of the promotion of agricultural efficiency. Agricultural science is to-day making rapid strides and large opportunities exist both for improving the quality and for cheapening the costs of agricultural production. Similar opportunities present themselves in connection with marketing arrangements. It is of the utmost importance that our farmers should be enabled to take advantage of these opportunities, and there is no better service that the State can render to agriculture than to facilitate and encourage the adoption of more efficient methods. Greater agricultural efficiency is the essential condition of a harmonious marriage between nutrition and agriculture.

The objectives which in our opinion should guide agricultural policy will now be clear to the reader. We may summarize them briefly as follows:

1. Protective measures should be limited as far as possible to the purpose of securing reasonable stability for home producers and averting disastrous fluctuations of prices. They should not be designed to reduce the volume of our food imports or to enlarge our home agricultural production of commodities that can more advantageously be produced abroad.

2. We should look to the development of British agriculture mainly in an increased production of "health foods," for which our farmers enjoy a high degree of natural protection, and in the improvement of the quality of British agricultural produce in general.

3. The promotion of greater efficiency both in production and marketing is a matter of the utmost importance; and State assistance should be given so far as possible in ways that are likely to promote efficiency.

4. An essential feature of agricultural policy should be the preservation of the fertility of the soil. The Government's grant towards cheapening fertilisers and the subsidy of £2 for each acre of grassland ploughed up before September 30, 1939, have been useful contributions towards this.

We think it important to add, however, that a governing consideration in applying these principles must be the avoidance of any really serious disturbance of British agricultural life. As our later chapters will make clear, we are unable to defend as permanently justifiable various of the existing measures of agricultural assistance. These measures have, none the less, served a useful purpose in sustaining agriculture in a period of great difficulty and we should deprecate any course which might result in throwing our farming back into the unsatisfactory conditions from which it has so recently emerged. The abandonment or modification of extravagant or inappropriate measures of assistance must, therefore, in our view, keep step with the progress that is made with other measures for the benefit of agriculture, and must depend to some extent on the results which such measures achieve.

The application of these principles will require us to survey in some detail the different branches of our agricultural life. Before attempting this task, however, we turn first to a survey of the changes that have occurred in British agriculture in the last seventy years.

CHAPTER III

THE CHANGING STRUCTURE OF BRITISH AGRICULTURE, 1866-1938

Introduction

IN 1866 the Agricultural Returns of Great Britain for the first time supplied an account of the acreage, the cropping and the livestock of the country.[1] For this reason any survey which is based on statistical evidence cannot go back further than 1866; in fact the Returns did not become complete enough to be reliable till 1870-1. From then on we can watch the constant changes in crops grown, in the various kinds of live-stock kept, and in methods of farm organization, by which the British agriculturalist has sought to adjust himself to the bewildering development of world food supplies.

There is another important reason for beginning our survey in that period. The American civil war was just over, and in the following years shipments to Britain of wheat, cheese and frozen meat began to attain proportions never before dreamed of. This fierce competition from overseas agriculturalists, working with equal skill under more favourable conditions, has been the dominant theme of British agriculture from the 'seventies down to the present day. We shall see in subsequent pages how our farmers were driven from one commodity to another, only to be caught up and beaten as soon as they became established in each new venture. Again and again British farmers have made these changes, first to meat, then to dairying, more recently to eggs and vegetables. They have applied overseas methods in so far as local conditions allowed; they have learnt to economize in the use of labour; they have adopted more scientific ways of manuring the land, and of feeding stock. Yet still only the best of them have done this

[1] Ernle: *English Farming, Past and Present.* 4th ed. 1936. p. 364.

successfully, and many of the less able or less fortunate have perforce abandoned the industry.

The second theme which runs through the period, is the continuous industrialization of Britain, with a rapid growth in the urban population and a steady rise in the workers' standard of living. This has had two effects of importance for agriculture. In the first place the expansion of industry and the obvious gap between industrial and agricultural wages have drawn workers away from the land at an accelerating speed and have forced up the wages of those remaining behind. In the second place the rise of large urban consuming centres and the rising standard of living have profoundly altered the character of the demand for food. Not only has there been a change in the type of food stuffs eaten, but also in the quality and regularity of supply demanded, a change which has had and is having far-reaching repercussions on the organization of agriculture.

These developments have gone forward more rapidly in Britain than in any major continental country, for the two interlocking reasons that our *tempo* of industrialization was the fastest in Europe and that the policy of free trade gave consumers a wider range of choice, while requiring of our farmers a greater adaptability of technique than was the case elsewhere. The result has been for the urban consumer a richer and more varied diet, absorbing a relatively small proportion of his wages. There have, of course, been periods, as during the depression of 1880–95, when the agricultural population suffered severely; and it is arguable that at such times appropriate measures of assistance would have eased their position without any prejudice to the national welfare. Nevertheless, it is true to say that, over the long period, the traditional British policy of putting the consumer first has benefited the agricultural worker, by drawing away redundant labour and raising wages, almost as much as the industrial worker. Protectionist countries, on the other hand, may have strengthened their national safety but have definitely retarded any improvement in the welfare of their peasant populations.

During the last seven years Britain, too, has pursued a protectionist policy, and it will be interesting to observe its effects in the changed conditions of to-day. But that must be reserved to later chapters of this book. First of all we have to examine changes in consumption and the growth of imports, and then discuss in some detail how different branches of agriculture and different parts of Britain have reacted to these new circumstances.

Consumption and the Standard of Living

Taken as a whole the period between the 'sixties and the (nineteen) 'thirties shows an unprecedented expansion in the quantity of food-stuffs absorbed by the British market. In the first place our population very nearly doubled itself from 1861 to 1931 so that, apart from any change in consumption *per head*, the nation required proportionately more food, an increase which could only be met with the help of imports. A similar growth of population occurred, of course, in other Western European countries, but they, at any rate the protectionist ones, countered it mainly by enlarging the agricultural area and by increasing the output per acre. Britain, on the other hand, had by 1870 taken almost as much land into cultivation as was profitable under a free-trade régime; after 1890 the area began to decline. Furthermore, the yield of crops per acre and the quality of live-stock in this country were at that time far in advance of general standards on the continent, so that, although improvement continued, there was not so much room for sensational advance as elsewhere. This was one of the principal reasons why our increasing food requirements had to be met mainly by imports.

But what the nation required was not just twice as much of the same types of food-stuffs as were eaten in the middle of the nineteenth century. If that had happened the British farmer would have been even worse off than he actually was, because it would have meant an increased demand concentrated mainly on wheat and the coarser food-stuffs. Fortunately, the growth of population was accompanied by an even faster growth in the national income, and hence by an increase in real incomes per head which caused a change in the type of foods consumed.

It is impossible to state definitely how much real incomes or real wages (which are more relevant to the demand for food) have risen since 1866; but after comparing various calculations which have been made, it appears that the rise in real wages was probably something between 70 and 90 per cent during the seventy years.[1] The development was not evenly distributed over the period. A rapid increase up to the end of the century was followed by a static period until about 1924, since when a further advance has occurred.

This change has brought about a quite startling revolution in diet, in particular an increase in the consumption of what are known to-day as the "protective" or health foods,[2] at the expense of or in addition to the coarser cereals or energy foods.

TABLE 1

Per capita consumption in lbs. per annum

	Wheat Flour	Potatoes	Sugar	Meat	Butter	Fruit	Vegetables
* 1861–5	252	—	35	100	—	—	—
† 1880	—	270	—	—	12	—	—
‡ 1911–13	211	208	79	135	16	61	60
§ 1936	212	213	94	148	25	114	126

* Layton: op. cit., p. 268.

† British Association, Wages Committee. Report 51st. Meeting. 1882.

‡ Orr: *Food, Health and Income*, p. 18.

§ Figures supplied by the Food (Defence Plans) Department.

[1] Cf. G. H. Wood's figures quoted by Layton: *Introduction to the Study of Prices*, 1935 ed., pp. 265–6. Bowley: *The Changes in the Distribution of the National Income*, 1880–1913. Pigou and Clark: *The Economic Position of Great Britain*, 1936.

[2] Dairy produce, fruit, vegetables and eggs.

The *per capita* consumption of butter has more than doubled, and a still greater increase would probably be seen in fruit and vegetables if we had figures for earlier years. Even the consumption of meat has increased 43 per cent, while, on the other hand, that of the main energy foods, wheat-flour and potatoes, has fallen, though the consumption of sugar, another energy food, has increased enormously.

Thus the population, besides increasing in numbers, has come in the main to eat more per head of those foods which the British farmer could more easily produce in competition with agriculturalists overseas. He enjoyed a clear advantage in producing meat of high quality; he had a similar advantage for most vegetables and temperate fruit. Even liquid-milk production proved capable of great expansion, because, although *per capita* consumption remained more or less constant, the total amount required almost doubled (with population) and enjoyed a naturally sheltered market.

What fragmentary evidence is available from continental countries suggests that although a similar trend is observable, it developed far more slowly. While *per capita* consumption of bread and probably of vegetables increased, that of meat, butter and sugar remained in most countries behind, and in some far behind, what it was in our country. An important factor in this connection has been the lower level of real wages in most countries on the continent.[1]

Another factor which stimulated consumption was the greater regularity of supply, brought about by the growth of imports which, in turn, was rendered possible by the development of storage technique. The fruit-eating season was extended, first, by the introduction of cheap tropical fruits, and later by the shipment of refrigerated apples and pears from the southern hemisphere. Eggs, too, came from an increasing number of different countries,

[1] On the other hand, in Denmark the use of sugar has increased more rapidly than in Britain, and consumption per head is now greater than it is here.

including the antipodes, which has helped to reduce the seasonal fluctuations in prices. These developments have tended to make the consumer more exacting in his demands for level delivery. Moreover, since he has migrated from a rural to an urban area, he inclines to forget that cows do not naturally give much milk in winter, without skilful and expensive management, nor do barn-yard fowls lay many eggs.

But besides requiring a regular supply, the present-day consumer demands a supply of uniform and reliable quality. Again, imports, which are more easily graded, have taught him the possibilities in this direction; and the distributors, both wholesalers and retailers, who handle a far larger proportion of the total food supplies than seventy years ago, have quickly learnt the convenience of dealing in dependable brands, of being able to repeat orders by telephone and receive both the exact quantity and exact quality desired. Only a special history of the food trade could bring out the subtle but important changes in this direction which have been going on during the last few decades and which are likely to continue.

Now both these factors, regularity of delivery and fixed standards of quality, have worked to the British farmer's disadvantage. For almost all types of crops he is dependent on the season, which the most skilful devices can do little to lengthen. It is true that he can attempt a less seasonal output of milk and eggs, and some advances along this line have been made in the last few years; but, as things are at present, winter costs of production remain inevitably higher than summer costs. As regards the problem of standardizing quality he is up against two difficulties. Firstly, it is always easier to adopt a grading system when supplies have to pass through the narrow channel of export agents; and attempts to counter this disadvantage, in particular the National Marks, have met with insufficient success as yet. Secondly, he is handicapped, unless he operates on a very large scale, by the smallness of his production unit. He will not have, on any one day, enough produce of any given quality to make up an adequate consignment. This point we shall see emphasized in the experience of the small market gardeners. Moreover, if the public in this matter develops a still more discriminating demand, it will probably cause wholesalers to deal still more with large growers at the expense of smallholders.

These then are the main features of the food market as it has developed during the last seventy years: an enormous increase in total requirements; a change towards a more varied diet, being mainly a shift from the cheaper, energy-supplying, to the dearer, health-protective foods; and a greater degree of service demanded, particularly as regards regularity and quality of supplies.

Imports

Already in the eighteen-sixties Britain imported a very considerable quantity of food-stuffs, but these consisted mainly of grain and of sugar; imports of live-stock products were still, relatively speaking, insignificant. Furthermore, the imports came chiefly from the eastern seaboard of the United States and other districts with which British farmers could still to some extent compete, especially in a period of rising prices.

During the next twenty years the situation completely changed. American farmers pushed across the Mississippi and past the Great Lakes, opening up new wheat lands, expanding cattle ranches and leaving the old-established eastern area to concentrate on dairy produce, especially cheese for export. Costs of production sank far below the level which obtained in Britain, and this, superimposed upon the sagging general level of prices from 1875 to 1895, was mainly responsible for the agricultural depression. All the aids of applied science could only mitigate; they could not avert the disaster. British farmers had drastically to change their farm practice or else go out of business.

"They were, in fact, confronted with a new problem. How were they to hold their own in a treacherous climate on highly rented land, whose fertility required constant renewal, against produce raised under more genial skies on cheaply rented soils, whose virgin richness needed no fertilizers."[1]

For a large section of the farming community retrenchment, not development, had to be the order of the day; yet it was not these who pulled through, but rather those with sufficient resources and/or ability to attempt producing new commodities by improved methods. Far-sighted men put perhaps half their farms down to grass, and built up a high-grade rearing or fattening business, or, as in some areas, increased the output of milk and butter.

This proved no more than a temporary escape. The early 'nineties saw a slackening of the United States' expansion, but elsewhere new areas were being opened up: Canada, the Argentine, Australia and New Zealand. The recently discovered methods of refrigeration made it commercially possible to ship meat and butter through the tropics without preserving in brine. Thus, as the table shows, in the period between 1891–5 and 1911-13 grain imports increased more slowly, while the sensational expansion was in imports of meat and butter. It was at this time, too, that Denmark first became an important food exporter.

TABLE 2

Annual Average Net Imports into the United Kingdom (thousand cwts.)

	Sugar	Wheat and Wheat Flour	All Grain and Meal excl. Wheat	Meat	Butter	Cheese
1861–5	11,814	34,652	25,585	1,553	1,031	771
1871–5	16,943	50,495	47,067	3,134	1,368	1,349
1891–5	28,288	96,583	78,475	10,437	2,409	2,150
1911–3	37,201	119,666	91,027	21,500	4,148	2,360
1925–9	36,200	109,500	69,472	31,043	6,600	3,020
1932–6	28,996	112,702	91,043	30,902	8,381	2,885

[1] Ernle: *English Farming Past and Present*, 4th ed., p. 380.

Again British farmers were caught; once again they were forced to re-orientate their production. This time the only hope seemed to be to concentrate on better quality produce: fresh meat could still compete against frozen meat, and good barley still stood at a premium. Fortunately, the beginning of the twentieth century was a time of rising prices and hence not so difficult for the farming community, though demands for better wages grew frequent. The Great War intervened just when labour troubles were beginning to become acute.

After the war a new phase of competition set in, more intense than any previous one, since it combined all the characteristics of previous phases and introduced certain novel features. In Canada, Australia and the Argentine a vast expansion of wheat acreage occurred, till each was exporting more than the United States did in the 'eighties. In addition to this, the invention of chilling made it possible for the Argentine to send meat which could compete with all but the finest qualities of British beef. New Zealand, thanks to a favourable climate and to efficiency, enormously expanded her butter and lamb exports at ever lower and lower prices. Denmark did the same with butter and eggs and bacon. Even fruit, of kinds and in seasons competitive with our own, was shipped in rapidly increasing quantities from North America.

In face of this there was nothing left for the British farmer but to concentrate on those products in which he enjoyed a naturally sheltered market; and so we witnessed a still swifter change-over from arable to grass farming, an enormous expansion in milk production supported by collective bargaining arrangements, and a doubling of the output of eggs and vegetables.

Those farmers who still grew crops and reared stock to compete with imports, had greatly to increase their technical efficiency in order to remain solvent. Particularly after 1924, when the wages of hired workers were brought under the control of County Committees, and came to be more and more divorced from the price level of agricultural produce, farmers were forced to economize labour in every possible way. This is instanced by the disappearance of mangolds and turnips and the substitution of green kale and sugar beet tops as cheaper forms of cattle food, by increased use of fertilizers on the land, by more scientific feeding of stock, by the spread of machinery of all kinds, particularly the tractor, and of course, by concentration upon products which require little labour or labour of a highly skilled kind.[1]

Since 1932 Britain has abandoned free trade; tariffs and/or quantitative restrictions have been imposed upon a wide range of agricultural products. As we saw in Chapter I, many of these measures were of a temporary nature, designed to protect farmers against a sudden and severe fall in prices, but they have also affected the volume of our food imports and the sources from which we draw our supplies. It may be useful to reproduce the following table showing changes in the volume of food imports over recent years, and also the change in the proportion coming respectively from Empire and foreign sources in 1936 as compared with 1927-9.

It is evident that the various restrictions which have been imposed have had a steadying effect upon the volume of food imports as a whole, though the effect on individual commododities has differed widely. During the period of economic depression these restrictive measures did substantially assist in preventing a flooding of the British

---

[1] Though the rural exodus will be more fully discussed in another chapter, it is important to remember that a rapid diminution in the agricultural population was the background to all these changes in farming. The exodus of labour was greatest in Scotland, chiefly from the crofting counties; in England the Midlands lost most, and, in recent years, West Wales. The only districts where numbers have been maintained are those adjacent to big industrial centres, districts specially suited to market-gardening or glass-house production. The density of agricultural labour *per acre of agricultural land* is actually highest near the biggest urban areas, London and Lancashire. It is lowest in the remote purely pastoral districts of Wales and Scotland.

TABLE 3

Index of Volume of Food Imports*
(1927–29 = 100)

Year	Meat including Bacon	Dairy Products	Eggs	Wheat	Vege- tables	Fruit	All
1927–9	100	100	100	100	100	100	100
1930	106	109	107	99	101	99	105
1931	117	123	104	110	156	120	117
1932†	112	127	84	96	142	118	111
1933	101	133	76	103	87	107	107
1934	94	142	81	95	81	88	104
1935	92	137	84	92	88	111	103
1936	92	138	102	92	100	88	105
1937	95	136	103	89	86	86	103
1937 Empire	144	161	63	130	136	174	142
Foreign	70	11 4	112	54	73	47	79

* Murray and Cohen: *The Planning of Britain's Food Imports*, Fourth Supplement. Oxford, Agricultural Economics Research Institute, 1938.

† Import duties and restriction schemes began to take effect during this year.

market; on the other hand they have not greatly retarded the normal growth of food imports. But the feature of this table is the large diversion which has been effected from imports from foreign countries to imports from the Empire. Incidentally, the fact that a large proportion of our food imports now comes from Empire countries renders it extremely difficult, as we shall notice again in our conclusions, to shield the British farmer from sudden vicissitudes in world market conditions. Actually, despite protection, farmers today have to compete with a slightly larger volume of supplies from abroad than they did ten years ago. They are witnessing, as in previous decades, the introduction of new technical devices which primarily benefit the overseas producer, and they are endeavouring, as always, to modify their methods and their farming practice in accordance with new developments.

In the remainder of this chapter we shall consider in more detail the extent of these changes in farm technique and organization over the seventy years as a whole. We shall see how British farmers have encountered the constant and difficult problems of adjustment, of economy and of technical development; and also how this has affected the balance of agricultural production.

Crops

The cropping of Britain had already been revolutionized a century before the official statistics begin. In the middle of the eighteenth century the introduction of turnips, and of clover which had been coming into use for some time previously, effected a greater revolution in agriculture than had ever occurred in its whole history. Briefly this had two results. It increased the available area for crops some 50 per cent, by doing away with the necessity for fallow on all but the heaviest lands. Still more important, it provided winter food for cattle and made possible the growth of the live-stock industry on a scale hitherto impossible. In addition, the increased number of live-stock meant more manure for the fields, and the hoeing of turnips caused the land to be kept clear of weeds; these together contributed towards a noteworthy rise in yields per acre, which was augmented still further during the nineteenth century when artificial fertilizers came into use.

It was the increased production per acre coupled with an increase in the area of land under cultivation, as enclosure continued, which made it possible for British agriculture to feed the growing industrial population. But by the middle of the nineteenth century only extremely infertile land remained unused, and so the still increasing population had to be provisioned more and more with supplies from overseas. This is the situation in 1870 when the curtain goes up and we can watch the scene changing from decade to decade.

The total area under crops and grass continued to rise steadily till 1891, the increase in permanent grass more than compensating for the decline in arable. Since then the total agricultural area, excluding rough grazing, has fallen from 32·9 to 29·3 million acres in 1937. These figures, however, are much open to question. It is probable that the increase in the returned acreage between 1871 and 1891 can be accounted for largely by the increasing accuracy of the returns; while in 1891 the category of "rough grazings" was included for the first time, and it is probable that some of the land which is now recorded as "rough grazings" would have ranked as "permanent pasture" before 1891. The recorded encroachment of rough grazings on to the cultivated land may, therefore, be more apparent than real.

The figures, as they stand, show that in the period 1891–1913 about 45,000 acres per annum went out of cultivation in Great Britain, of which half was lost to rough grazings and half to non-agricultural uses. Since 1913 the loss has been much more rapid; over 100,000 acres per annum, of which three-quarters has gone to rough grazing and only one-quarter to other uses.[1] It is within this steadily shrinking agricultural acreage that the more generally known modifications, such as the decline in the corn area and the laying down of land to grass, have taken place.

The area under permanent grass has increased by over 40 per cent (1870–1937). The expansion has been greatest and most sustained in Scotland; indeed in England and Wales the pasture area is actually less to-day than in 1913. This is not because England and Wales have changed less from arable to pasture farming than has Scotland, but because they have lost far more land to rough grazing. The grassland area has increased most in Devon and Cornwall and in the home counties[2] (excluding Surrey

[1] It is likely that some of the increase in rough grazings since 1913 is due to a gradual change in the definition of what is "rough."

[2] This and all subsequent comparisons by county have been worked out as a percentage change on the 1870–1 acreage of the particular crop.

and Middlesex where the inroads of building have dominated). Probably this is connected with the growth of dairying
in these areas. In Scotland the expansion of pasture is more
evenly distributed, perhaps slightly greater in the south-
eastern counties. Altogether the proportions of arable to
permanent grass have been almost reversed; whereas to-day
Britain is a carpet of grass with a pattern of arable, in
1870 it was a carpet of arable with a pattern of grass.

The arable area has declined steadily and substantially.
In the last sixty-seven years an area greater than that of the
whole of Wales has been lost to the plough. But the decline
has proceeded at very different speeds in different districts.
It has shrunk least of all in the districts where the climate
is best suited to the cultivation of corn crops, i.e. the east-
coast counties of England and in Aberdeenshire. It has
also changed little in the hilly regions of Wales, Cumberland and the Highlands where it was already at a minimum.
It has declined most in those counties where alternatives
of employment for the labourers were many, and where
urban and suburban development made milk production
particularly profitable. Thus up to 1913 the decline was
greatest in the Midlands and the North-East of England,
where the staple industries still prospered. Since the Great
War the decline has been concentrated in the south-midland
and southern counties where new industries were springing
up. Similarly in Scotland the decline has been centred
round the densely populated industrial belt from Fife to
Renfrew. But because in Scotland oats rather than wheat
is the principal crop the change has, on the whole, been
less marked, the total decline in arable acreage over sixty-
seven years being 15 per cent compared with 48 per cent in
England and Wales. There has, however, been a general
development of cultivation northwards which is noticeable
in the case of both arable land and permanent grass. This
is unquestionably part of the general push towards the
pole which is a noteworthy feature of all the northern
countries, and which has been made possible mainly by
improvements in the breeding of plants.

Among the individual corn crops the principal decline has been in barley; only just over a third as much was grown in 1937 as in 1870, and the barley area has become increasingly concentrated in Norfolk, Suffolk, Lincolnshire and the East Riding. The wheat acreage is about half as great as in 1870; though an interesting feature is the increase in wheat production in the east of Scotland, no doubt due to the introduction of hardier wheats. The area under oats, on the other hand, has only declined by about one-fifth; and this decline has all occurred within the last twenty years, largely as a result of farm horses being replaced by tractors. This crop has always been grown chiefly for feeding to stock on the farm, hardly at all for sale.

Most of the other field crops—turnips, swedes, mangolds, peas, beans, etc.—have had to face rather a similar form of competition. The costs of producing these various crops have steadily risen, while other kinds of feeding-stuffs, such as imported feed-grain and oil-cake, have become progressively cheaper. For this reason, despite our much larger live-stock population, we produce less food for animals than seventy years ago; indeed, no fodder crop, except grass and hay, is grown on so large a scale now as then. Among these crops some have become particularly costly to grow, and these have disappeared faster than the others. It has been mainly those crops which required a large amount of manual labour in their cultivation, since the price of farm labour has risen more than any other element in costs. Thus the acreage under turnips and swedes was in 1937 just over one-third of what it was in 1870; the area under peas and beans is less than a third of what it was, and the acreage under vetches and tares has declined in a similar proportion. The mangold acreage, on the other hand, actually increased till 1914, and has only shrunk rapidly in the last fifteen years owing to the rise of the sugar beet industry It is indeed the sugar subsidy which has prevented the area under roots from declining more rapidly.

The following figures sum up the extent of the decline in the principal types of crops:

TABLE 4

Decline in Crop Acreage

	Corn Crops million acres	Root Crops million acres	Rotation Crops million acres
1870	9½	3⅔	4½
1937	5	2	3⅔

The areas under corn and root crops have declined by 47 and 46 per cent respectively, whereas the area under rotation grasses has only declined by 19 per cent, partly because these grass crops require less labour, and partly because they are grown almost entirely to be consumed on the farm.

Now an important effect of the gradual changes in cropping during the last seventy years has been a substantial modification of the system of rotations.[1] These modifications are of two kinds; firstly, in the actual rotation followed, and secondly, in the kind of crop grown in a particular break. In a typical four-course rotation we should expect to find almost exactly half the land under cereals, one-quarter under roots (green crops), and the other quarter under "seeds."

TABLE 5

Percentage of Total "Rotation" Crops Acreage

Crops	England & Wales		Scotland	
	1870	1937	1870	1937
	%	%	%	%
Cereals:				
Corn (exclud. Peas and Beans)	49·5	45·5	40·2	34·0
Peas and Beans . . .	5·6	2·3	0·7	0·1
Roots:				
Green and Root Crops .	19·5	18·6	20·7	16·3
Bare Fallow . . .	4·0	6·3	0·7	0·5
Other Crops (mostly roots) .	—	1·3	—	0·3
Rotation Grasses . . .	21·4	26·0	38·5	48·8

[1] Not that there ever was a standard rotation; because, though the Norfolk four-course may have been typical, there were always certain areas practising adaptations of their own; e.g., a three-year shift of

It will be seen that if we exclude the acreage under peas and beans and bare fallow, most of which fall outside the regular four-course rotation, in 1870 the four-course rotation must have been very common, at any rate in England, giving a corn: roots: grass ratio of 2: 1: 1:[1] By 1937 the proportion of rotation grasses to the total had increased in both England and Scotland; in Scotland half the arable area was under rotation grasses, one-sixth under roots and one-third under corn; this would be given by a rotation such as roots, corn, seeds, seeds, seeds, corn.

Within each class of crop there is, of course, a much greater degree of flexibility as to what is grown. Thus oats have been displacing barley in the corn crops.[2] Similarly potatoes and sugar beet have been displacing

beans, wheat, fallow, on soils too stiff to grow roots; an eight or nine-year course in the Lothians where the seeds break was extended.

[1] In Scotland even at that date it is evident that the two-year seeds ley must have been prevalent, and probably the distribution of the various crops in Scotland in 1870 would have been given by a rotation such as roots, corn, seeds, seeds, corn, giving a corn: roots: seeds ratio of 2 : 1 : 2.

[2] This is seen in the following table:

TABLE 6

Percentage of Total Corn Crop Acreage

Crops	England & Wales		Scotland	
	1870	1937	1870	1937
	%	%	%	%
Wheat	46·2	44·5	9·0	10·0
Barley	29·2	21.3	17·5	8·1
Oats	23·9	31·4	72·8	81·5
Rye	0·7	0·4	0·7	0·2
Mixed Corn. . . .	—	2·4	—	0·2

turnips in the root break;[1] and there is, of course, wide flexibility in the type of seeds used in the seeds break although we have no statistics on this point.

A further aspect of the British farmer's effort to adapt himself to changing conditions is illustrated by the history of the *yields* of crops. There are strong *a priori* reasons for expecting yields to have increased over a period of nearly seventy years. On the one hand scientific research has produced better and ever better strains of seeds, and healthier and higher-yielding varieties. On the other hand the total amount of manure of all descriptions which is placed annually on the soil of this country, has almost certainly been increasing since 1870, for apart altogether from the use of artificial fertilizers, the total number of animals has increased appreciably.[2] In these circumstances it is all the more surprising that the yield of crops has shown so little change. The yields of a number of crops are shown in the following table:

[1] The proportion of different root crops in the root break has changed in the following manner:

TABLE 7

Percentage of Total Root Crop Acreage

Crops	England & Wales		Scotland	
	1870	1937	1870	1937
	%	%	%	%
Potatoes	14·8	27·7	26·5	27·1
Sugar Beet	—	18·6	—	1·3
Turnips and Swedes . .	67·3	26·8	72·8	66·5
Mangolds	12·2	12·6	0·2	0·2
Cabbage, Kohl Rabi and Rape	5·7	14·3	0·5	4·4

[2] It is true that the number of horses has been declining, and that the sheep population has been moving off the arable land on to the grassland; nevertheless even in the arable areas this has been more than compensated by an increase of 50–100 per cent, according to district, in the number of cattle.

TABLE 8

Average Yield per Acre of the Principal Farm Crops in Great Britain in Ten-Year Periods from 1886–95 to 1926–35

Period	Wheat	Barley	Oats	Pota-toes	Tur-nips and Swedes	Man-golds	Hay from Clover, Sainfoin and Rotation Grasses	Hay from Perma-nent Grass
	Bush.	Bush.	Bush.	Tons	Tons	Tons	Cwt.	Cwt.
1886–95	28·8	32·7	38·2	5·9	13·4	17·6	28·1	23·4
1896–1905	31·2	33·0	38·9	5·8	13·0	18·7	29·1	23·5
1906–15	32·2	33·1	39·7	6·3	14·2	19·3	29·6	23·2
1916–25	31·4	31·2	38·9	6·2	13·7	19·1	29·1	21·4
1926–35	32·3	34·0	43·9	6·5	13·3	18·7	28·2	20·0

* We may take the average yield of crops in Great Britain as a fairly significant average: Great Britain to a very large extent is a climatic unit, and good and bad weather is usually fairly generally distributed.

Since 1886 the yield of cereals and of potatoes has risen slightly, the yield of turnips, mangolds and seeds hay first increased and later declined, while the yield of meadow hay has fallen. An analysis of the year to year figures suggests that the violence of the annual fluctuations has been decreasing, showing either a greater control over the effect of climate or perhaps merely a change towards a less extreme climate; the evidence is not conclusive.

The slight rise in the yields of arable crops and the slight fall in the yield of hay are easily accounted for by the movement which has taken place in the areas under these crops. As we have seen, arable cultivation has been receding into those parts of the country most suited to it. We should expect a rise in the average yield of crops for this reason alone, and the wonder is that the rise has not been greater. Similarly, permanent grass has been encroaching on areas in the eastern part of the country which are not naturally so suited to it, and we should in consequence expect the yield to fall. The general conclusion must be, therefore, that in the past few decades taking one crop with another the general yield per acre in this country has been stationary, though, at the same time, in districts where high farming is still practised the yields have increased substantially. It is probable that two forces affecting yield have been balancing each other; the advance of scientific knowledge on the one hand, and the movement towards a lower intensity of farming on the other. In this respect it is interesting to notice that in the case of turnips and mangolds the gains in yield were made before 1914; since the war yields have been declining; indeed, the rapid decline in the arable acreage since the war seems to have gone hand in hand with a generally lower "land intensity" of farming.

The reason for this is clear. The price of labour has risen very fast while the price of land has been stationary or has fallen. In the days when a farmer could employ a large amount of labour he had every root crop hoed several times, kept down the weeds and secured high yields not only of roots but also of cereals in the following year. To-day labour must be foregone and the crop left to look after itself; indeed were it not for the increased use of organic manures and the invention of various machines which economize labour in cultivation, crop yields would inevitably have fallen more.

An alternative method of adaptation has been to increase the output of certain special crops for which prices have been better maintained, notably vegetables and fruit. A number of general farmers have in recent years introduced vegetables into their ordinary rotation. Generally speaking the enterprise has proved highly profitable, and has in many cases saved the whole rotational system from having to be abandoned. But although the vegetable acreage has nearly doubled in fifteen years, it is still quantitatively unimportant: less than a quarter of a million acres altogether. Another recent development has been the increase in fruit acreage. Commercial fruit-growing has become a highly skilled and largely specialized business. In consequence, after many years of stagnation and even of slight decline, the area under orchard fruit increased by some 14,000 acres to 258,000 acres during the period 1931–7, the new planting being mainly of high-grade apples. Good quality fruit still fetches prices which sufficiently cover the rather high costs incurred in production.

Apart from these rather special developments, it is the steadily increasing cost of labour which appears a predominant driving force behind the various alterations in the structure of farming. In every principal crop there has been a decline in acreage, but particularly in those which require a large amount of manual labour. In every district also there has been a decline, but most of all in those where alternative opportunities for employment have been favourable.

This is a tendency generally observable in countries where a rising urban standard of living draws labour out of agriculture. It leads first to an increase of live-stock in general, and then later on to specialization in those live-stock products which require least labour and have the quickest turnover. We can now turn to the development of live-stock farming to see how this change-over has occurred in our own country.

Live-stock

(i) Cattle

During the last seventy years the cattle population of Great Britain has increased by nearly 50 per cent; in England and Wales the expansion was greater and in Scotland proportionately less. Although there is considerable interconnection between the beef and dairying branches of the cattle industry, it is important, in view of their differing circumstances, to follow the development of each separately.

During the great agricultural depression of the 'eighties and early 'nineties farmers began to turn more attention to beef production. Even though cattle prices were nearly as bad as wheat prices, it proved less unprofitable to feed crops into stock than to sell grain in the open market, since at least one had the dung as a by-product. Hence the greatest expansion of cattle feeding took place in those arable areas most hit by the fall in wheat prices, that is, down the eastern side of England and in certain midland counties; the expansion was far less in Scotland, since Scottish farmers, being interested primarily in oats, had never looked upon cereals principally as cash crops, and so were less affected by depressed prices. On the other hand Wales, with scarcely any arable farming at all, developed her live-stock business as rapidly as England developed fattening, mainly to provide the English feeders with stores, but partly to supply finished beasts to the expanding industrial populations of South Wales, the Midlands and South Lancashire.

After the Great War the situation changed. English and Welsh farmers found milk a more attractive line than beef-cattle; accordingly the beef-cattle population stagnated and was in 1937 at much the same level as in 1913.[1] In Scotland, where the attractive alternative was not available to any great extent, the pre-war rate of growth of the cattle industry has been maintained. There are other reasons why beef production had ceased to expand in England. London and the southern counties have come more and more to prefer Argentine chilled beef, imports of which have risen steadily. In Northern England, although the industrial population of the North still buys, in the main, home-produced beef, protracted and widespread unemployment have seriously impaired purchasing power and reduced the demand for meat.

Another aspect of the beef industry worthy of remark

[1] The figures for "Other Cattle," i.e. all cattle except cows in milk or in calf, and heifers in calf, have been taken to indicate roughly the quantitative changes in the home beef industry. This, however, inevitably includes the female calves destined for the dairy herd, but not old enough to be in the category of "Heifers in Calf."

is the earlier age at which animals are now brought to maturity. A far smaller proportion are kept over the age of two than formerly; thus in the beef herd the proportion "two years and over" has fallen from 40 per cent in 1870 to 28 per cent in 1937. The most rapid change has taken place during the last decade when the number of cattle "between one and two years" has grown rapidly while the number "two years and over" has actually declined. This must be attributed partly to the public demand for smaller joints, but chiefly to improvements in the technique of feeding, so that animals gain the desired weight in fewer months. Some farmers even manage to pass two sets of beasts through their stock-yards during the winter season.

Turning now to the dairy herd[1] we find a more modest rate of growth in the pre-war period (1870–1913). In England, it is true, the herd expanded about as fast as the numbers of beef-cattle, but not in Wales and Scotland. On the other hand this slow increase in cow population may have been consistent with quite a substantial increase in milk output. We know what an interest was taken in breeding, particularly when economic conditions in farming improved during the period 1895–1913, and this must have influenced milk yields, though there is no positive evidence.

After the war a very different situation developed. In England and Wales collective bargaining was carried on for farmers by the National Farmers' Union and the National Federation of Dairymen's Associations, so that the price of milk was kept at a higher level compared with pre-war than the prices of other agricultural commodities. This induced a number of farmers to increase their dairy herds, lay down fields to grass, and give up stock-fattening and/or the cultivation of field-crops for sale. At the same time the London milk distributors gradually began to move out further west and north to obtain supplies.

[1] Represented roughly by "cows in milk and calf" and "heifers in calf."

As a result of all this the dairy herd in England was 36 per cent higher in 1937 than in 1913, while in Wales the increase has been rather slower owing to natural and economic disadvantages. For the two regions together total milk *production* has increased by over 40 per cent since the 1908 Census. Very different has been the experience of Scotland. There the dairy herd has remained stationary or even fallen slightly. Scottish farmers were too far away to take advantage of the expanding liquid milk market in the south of England, and the nearer industrial centres underwent too severe a depression for *per capita* consumption to increase to any degree. Thus, except for a special development of milk production in certain favoured areas, Scotland has remained perforce a rearing and feeding country, so that actually the proportion of cows to "total cattle" has *declined* slightly since 1870, whereas in England and Wales the proportion has rapidly increased as dairying came to predominate over beef production.

(ii) *Sheep*

The British sheep population has undergone during the past seventy years most startling fluctuations, from close on 28 millions in 1870 down to 20 millions in 1922, back to 26½ millions in 1932 and receding to 24·7 millions in 1937. But apart from this general movement important differences in regional development must be noted. While in Scotland, and still more in Wales, the number of sheep has increased over the period taken as a whole, it has declined very steadily in England. The sheep-barley combination, which was once the mainstay of mixed farming on the chalk uplands of the south and east, and also on the west-midland plateau, has now disappeared, partly as a result of the unprofitableness of wheat and barley, and partly owing to the progressively rising costs of labour, which play such a large part in the cultivation of the crops, in moving the folds and in watering the flocks.

The old system crumbled away slowly. After a decline in the 'seventies, the total numbers remained fairly stable, but the sheep were shifting northward and westward, away from the land south of the Severn and Trent. The Great War hastened this process. Heavy slaughterings of stock depleted the sheep population; subsequently, after normal trade had been restored, farmers found great difficulty in maintaining the traditional system. Wheat, barley and mutton prices were low; wages stood high. Reluctantly farmers shifted more and more away to grass and dairy-herds or, in some counties, to sugar beet and to more cattle-feeding. The farming of the Wiltshire and Dorset downs, of the Lincoln and Yorkshire Wolds has thus been largely transformed from a mixed arable-sheep system to a mixed dairy system based on either arable or grass. The more able farmers are still capable of making even arable-sheep farming pay, yet the recovery in the sheep population has not occurred on their holdings, but is due rather to an increased stocking of the Welsh and Lakeland hills. This change has had some effect on the breeds of sheep favoured. The Downs arable sheep have made way for the Cross-Breds, Border-Leicesters and other types which fatten easily on grass.

Development in Scotland has been on rather different lines owing to the different structure of Scottish arable farming. Depending less on the sale of corn crops Scottish farmers could carry on, provided sheep and wool prices did not collapse too; furthermore, they had not such profitable openings in the liquid milk market as English farmers had. As a result, sheep not only maintained their position on the arable farms of eastern Scotland, but rapidly increased in numbers.

Just as in the case of cattle, so sheep are fattened for slaughter much earlier than in the old days; furthermore, the proportion killed as fat lambs has increased rapidly since the Great War. Thus sheep "under one year" used to form a third of the total population and now form nearly half. One would have expected this change to be more marked in England than in Wales and Scotland, where breeding predominates; yet strangely enough the age distribution seems to have altered to an equal extent in all three parts of Great Britain.

Having now concluded a review of the movements in the cattle and sheep population, we must consider, before going on to the small live-stock, what effects this has had on farm organization. Both the history of crops and the recent history of sheep have shown a weakening of the position of the mixed arable farmer. To-day some farmers say that stock fattening does not pay, but they need the dung; others say that to grow corn does not pay, but they need food for their stock; till the outsider has a shrewd suspicion that a traditional ritual is being performed, no part of which is really profitable. Probably this is an unfair view in most cases, but the subject merits attention, since mixed farming is still the core of British agriculture.

Mixed arable farming had its natural justification when farming was a way of life and each man tried to keep himself in bread and meat. Subsequently, improvements in corn growing and stock raising created surpluses for sale, and cash income gradually became the main interest of all but the smallest mixed farmers. Mixed farming still remained, however, the only method of producing meat and bread; the farmer had to grow food for the animals and he needed manure for his fields. But this natural combination has been upset by the introduction of certain new factors. The growth of imports has meant that the prices of the principal agricultural products have come to depend primarily upon the state of the world market. At any given moment one of the live-stock products, perhaps, and one of the crops might be profitable to the British farmer, whilst for all the others the price was too low; yet by his system of farming he was bound to produce all or none.

Another new factor was the development of manufactured cattle foods and the importation of cheap feed-grain. Hitherto live-stock could only be reared on the produce of one's own (or one's neighbour's soil); but now one's neighbour in that sense might be an Argentine maize-grower, and British farmers had to choose whether it would be cheaper to buy feeding-stuffs or to grow them themselves. Theoretically it would be possible to do without arable enterprise altogether and to feed the animals entirely on grass, hay, and bought food, but the practical choice has in effect been how much to buy and how much to grow. This decision is complicated by the possible profit on the cash crops which will come in the course of the rotation, so that it may pay a farmer to grow turnips for his bullocks *if* he can sell at 35s. a quarter the barley which will follow next year: whereas if barley is going to fall to 32s. it perhaps would pay him to put these fields down to grass now and buy feed for his beasts.

A third complicating factor emerged in the latter part of last century—artificial fertilizers. It was henceforward not strictly necessary to have any animals on the farm in order to carry on the rotation. In the extreme case one could grow, at least on most soils, roots, barley, seeds, wheat, year after year, simply by applying to the soil the right kinds of chemicals. Again, in practice the farmer had to decide what middle course to pursue, how much manure he should buy and how much he should obtain from live-stock, bearing in mind the relative prices and the condition of his land. But the various farm enterprises are so intertwined that it is difficult to make a wise decision in advance. If the price of fat stock falls, the organic manure obtained from them has probably cost the farmer a quite uneconomic sum, and he would have done better to buy artificials. This, however, assumes that his crops are profitable in themselves, which in turn depends, as we saw above, on the price of alternative feeding-stuffs, on the price of the imports which compete with his cash crops, and, incidentally, on the price of manures!

The mixed farmer is apparently faced with a dismaying number of variables. The value of his two-end products, crops and stock, each depends on the fluctuations of world prices, and if one of the two is profitable the other can be justified as its auxiliary. But both the profitability of the one and the justification for the other depend on a wise choice of the alternative means of producing them, buying or growing his feeding-stuffs, buying his manures or producing them himself as a by-product. Rule of thumb methods have to be supplemented by money computations and estimates; hence more and more farmers are coming to keep accounts, though the majority still proceed by instinct, feeling all the time that something is wrong, yet without knowing where the trouble lies. Even accounts can only help a farmer to a certain extent; they cannot reveal the future state of markets. Nevertheless, it is necessary to emphasize that considerable business acumen, as well as a high degree of technical skill, is necessary to-day to the carrying-on of mixed arable farming. But while the mixed farmer has greater choice of policy and therefore greater chance of going wrong than he had two generations ago, it still remains true that mixed farming tends to be a safer investment than specialized farming, which risks all on a single product; and this advantage may be substantial in periods of economic uncertainty.

(iii) Pigs

The production of pigs has always been treated as a sideline by British farmers, although pigs contribute some 10 per cent to the value of the agricultural output. On the whole the pig population remained remarkably steady during the forty years from 1870 to 1910, though this bare statement masks certain regional differences. In most of Scotland and in the hill countries of Wales there was some decline, counteracted by a marked increase in particular districts elsewhere, particularly Cornwall, Suffolk, Lancashire and round Edinburgh. It is difficult to account for these local peculiarities because no marked change in the cropping (such as an increase in potato acreage) occurred in any of those four areas.

After the emergency slaughterings of the Great War

the pig population rapidly recovered, and throughout the 'twenties oscillated between 2½ and 3 millions, a higher figure than in pre-war days. The post-war recovery was mainly in the eastern counties of England and Scotland, partly, no doubt, a sign of the arable farmers' attempt to find more profitable lines of production. In the Highlands and in most of Wales the decline continued. But since the restriction of imports and the introduction of the Pig Marketing Scheme in 1933, the pig population of Great Britain has increased suddenly by about 40 per cent.

Pigs have never in this country been dovetailed in with any other agricultural product. They do not "hang on the cow's tail" as in Denmark, but flourish rather according to the condition of the farmer's other enterprises and according to the price of feeding-stuffs. Their geographical distribution bears some relation to the potato acreage but they are also concentrated in the neighbourhood of large towns.

Notwithstanding the relative unimportance of pigs, there has developed, at any rate since 1891, a noticeable four-year pig-cycle similar to that experienced in other countries. After the Great War it seemed to be working with particular regularity, but the inception of the Marketing Boards and the fixing of contract prices have somewhat modified its trend.

The quality of British pigs contrasted unfavourably with the quality of our sheep and cattle, until the recent drive to capture the home bacon market has forced farmers to realize the necessity for improvement. We had, of course, our pedigree herds, and some breeders earned substantial sums by exporting prize-winning boars to continental countries; but the general race of stock was poor in build and ill-adapted to making the right type of flesh; they were often badly housed, haphazardly fed and a prey to disease. Attempts are now being made to remedy these defects.

(iv) *Poultry*

No very reliable estimates of the numbers of poultry in Great Britain were made until the Ministry of Agriculture's census in 1908, when it was estimated that the total number of fowls was somewhere in the region of 37 million.[1] There had probably been some increase in the decades immediately preceding that census. It was a period of great experimentation with breeds, many of them only to please the fancier, but many being genuine attempts to find good egg-laying strains, different types suiting different soils.

It is also likely, therefore, that the figure of 72 eggs per bird per annum, given in that census, was an improvement on the yields of the 'seventies and 'eighties.

Between 1908 and 1924 a small increase in the number of hens was accompanied by a big increase in egg-yields per bird, so that the total egg output increased by some 50 per cent to just under 2,000 million per annum. Since then the development has been the most sensational feature in British farming:

TABLE 9

Poultry in Great Britain

	Total number of Fowls*	Output of:	
		Eggs	Table Poultry
	millions	*millions*	*,000 cwt.*
1924	36·1	1,973	989
1934	69·4	4,399	1,636

* These figures refer to poultry on holdings of "1 acre and above." An addition of about 33 per cent to the totals was thought by the Ministry of Agriculture sufficient to cover the production from allotments, private gardens, etc., in 1924.

[1] 28·2 million on holdings of "one acre and above" plus a rough estimate of poultry on other holdings.

It appears that in ten years the poultry population nearly doubled and the production of eggs more than doubled.[1] Since 1934, however, there has been a certain decline.

An examination of the districts in which the development took place will provide some clues as to the underlying reasons. The growth was concentrated in three regions: the southern counties—Wiltshire, Dorset, Hants; the eastern counties—Norfolk, Suffolk, Essex; and the northern industrial area—Lancashire and Durham. The first two districts suffered particularly from the difficulties which mixed arable farming has encountered, so that farmers in these areas paid more serious attention to building up the poultry flock, which previously was rather scoffed at as "the wife's affair." Although in these areas a certain number of poultry specialists established themselves either as smallholders or as large commercial egg-farmers, the development on general farms has probably been the more important. In Lancashire and Durham, on the other hand, poultry-keeping grew up in the hands of small specialist producers, and it was largely the continued industrial depression which brought so many new men into the business. Profits for some years were big enough to tempt poultry-keepers to expand production, for, even during the depression, feeding costs fell more or less parallel with egg prices.

Since 1908 the proportion contributed by poultry and eggs to the value of the total agricultural output has increased from $3\frac{1}{2}$ per cent to $10\frac{1}{2}$ per cent. For the five years 1931-5 the output from poultry was of greater value than the output from pigs. The poultry industry, therefore, has won an important place in the agriculture of this country, which is likely to be consolidated. It is an enterprise possessing the advantages of a rapid capital turnover and a very high gross output per acre and per man, these being important advantages in agriculture to-day. Nevertheless, if other farm enterprises continue to receive assistance, it

[1] The 1930–1 agricultural census showed egg-yields per bird to have increased in six years from 100 to 120.

is unlikely that the poultry industry will again expand so rapidly as in the period 1924-34.

The Agricultural Output

We can now conclude this discussion of the separate branches of farming with a few remarks on the changes in the agricultural output as a whole. It might be supposed that, consequent upon the enormous exodus of the agricultural population and the steady shrinkage in the arable acreage, the output of British agriculture would have greatly diminished. In this matter one must distinguish the *gross* from the *net* agricultural output.

No estimates, so far as we know, were made of the total value of the gross agricultural output until 1908. So the only means of arriving at an idea of the course of earlier developments is to take the statistics of acreages and livestock population in 1870, and, on certain assumptions, to estimate the quantity of output which they would produce; and then to value these quantities at the prices ruling in a census year.[1] Naturally the margin of error must be large, for we do not know how the average slaughter weight or age of fat stock has changed, nor milk-yields per cow, nor the egg-yields per hen, etc. Nevertheless, a careful examination of the available statistics suggests that the quantum of output increased by *something between* 30 per cent and 45 per cent during the sixty years 1870-1930.[2] Now the Ministry of Agriculture had estimated the increase in output between 1908 and 1930-1 at 4 per cent; therefore, reducing our tentative figure by this amount, our estimate of the expansion of output between 1870 and 1908 would be about 25-40 per cent. It would be unwise to put a more precise figure and probably the lower is nearer to the truth.[3]

[1] Actually we have used 1930-1 prices which were the most detailed available.

[2] Valued at 1870 prices the increase would appear smaller (because of the change in the relative prices of corn and live stock); therefore the true change is nearer 30 than 45 per cent.

[3] This estimate is very close to one worked out by Dr. Drescher: *Weltwirtschaftliches Archiv*, March 1935.

Since 1908 we are on surer ground. An official estimate of the gross output[1] was made in connection with the Agricultural Census of 1908, and this was repeated at the censuses of 1925 and 1930-1, since when annual estimates have been made.

TABLE 10

Quantum of Gross Output (1908=100)

1908	.	.	100
1925	.	.	100
1930–1	.	.	104
1934–5	.	.	123
1935–6	.	.	117
1936–7	.	.	122

Apart from the war period, no expansion took place between 1908 and 1925; but during the subsequent years output began to increase, and during the recent depression increased very considerably with the stimulus of protection and subsidies.

It is mainly meat, milk and eggs which have been responsible for this development. Since 1908 the proportion contributed by farm crops to the total output has declined from some 30 per cent to about 17 per cent in 1934-5 and would have been still lower but for the assistance given to sugar-beet and wheat. Before 1908 an analogous change-over from crops to live-stock must also have been in progress. Thus, although the area of agricultural land is smaller and although there are fewer people engaged in the industry than in 1870, yet the gross output, taken as a whole, is substantially greater.

To a certain extent this reflects an increase in productive efficiency (cows giving more milk, hens laying more eggs, mechanical cultivation reducing labour requirements, and so forth), but principally it shows that agriculture in this country has become more of a processing industry, purchasing raw materials (feeding-stuffs) from abroad and working

[1] i.e. the output sold to the non-agricultural community together with the amounts consumed in farm households.

them up into food-stuffs through the agency of the live-stock population. If we consider Britain and the Dominions as an economic unit, land has been plentiful. Accordingly specialization developed, the crops being grown in the "open spaces" overseas and converted into live-stock produce at home near the centres of urban demand. The volume of the principal feeding-stuffs imported into this country has grown from a total of 3·2 million tons in 1871-5 to 6·5 million tons in 1911-13 and to 7·8 million tons in 1935-7.[1] Although an exact computation is impossible, it seems almost certain that the *net* output of British agriculture has declined over the past seventy years, i.e. the gross output minus the imported raw materials of the industry. It is quite certain that between 1931 and 1937 the *net* output did not increase to any great extent for the volume of feeding-stuffs imported rose from 6·8 million tons to 8·1 million tons. All this represents a change in response to the shifting levels of prices, an increased use of raw materials and a decreased use of British land and British labour.

The farmer has been constantly adjusting his practice to this general trend. It has meant for him not merely the giving up of certain crops or the adoption of certain mechanical aids to production, but a re-adaptation of every branch of farm activity. It has meant experimentation in new treatments for grassland, new management of grazing, new combinations of feeds for the animals, new importance attached to enterprises hitherto ignored—such as vegetables and poultry. This process of change and re-adjustment is, of course, still taking place, and a large number of the present difficulties of agriculture, which will occupy us in succeeding chapters, arise from the not always successful efforts of farmers to keep abreast of modifications in world economic conditions and in technique.

[1] Including all imported oil-cake, maize, oats and corn offals; and assuming for the purposes of computation that half the imported barley is used for live-stock, one-quarter of the imported wheat (in the form of offals) and two-thirds by weight of the imported oil-seeds and nuts, the remainder being expressed as oil.

PART TWO
CROPS

CHAPTER IV

GRASS

THE aspect of the English scene which impresses itself most vividly on the imagination of the ordinary observer is its rich green grasslands. In places the pattern of the landscape may be varied with dark patches of cultivated land, but the abiding picture left on the mind is of continuous fields and meadows of brightest green. This is "England's green and pleasant land", and is not a mere fanciful picture. Actually about four-fifths of the entire country is under grass of some kind or other—a fact which many people think is to be deplored. The land is being lost to the plough. It is tumbling into grass. If this goes on where are the people to get their food in time of national emergency? These are the popular misconceptions about the land which are sometimes summed up in the expression "the tragedy of agriculture". It is very important, therefore, to see this question of grass in its true relation to the agricultural scheme of things in this country. When examined it will be found that the dominance of grass in our land is not a matter for regret. We have certain natural advantages for its production. Our climate is mild in winter and summer. The rainfall is ample and fairly evenly distributed throughout the year. We are not subject to the severe droughts and extremes of temperature from which many other European countries suffer. Indeed, few countries of the world enjoy such a favourable grass climate as Great Britain. The question before us, therefore, is how best we may turn these natural advantages to the benefit of agriculture and the welfare of the nation as a whole.

99

Varieties of Grassland

There are three kinds of grassland in Britain—permanent grass, rough grazing and (arable) temporary grass. Of the 30 million acres of land used for agriculture in England and Wales, about 23 million acres are under grass and 7 million acres under crops. Of the 23 million acres of grass, 15½ are permanent, 5½ are rough grazing (hills and heath land) and 2 million are temporary (sown with grass and clover like any other crop for a term of years and then ploughed up). In fact over 2 million acres of "arable" is in temporary grass leys. But of course there is no hard and fast division between the different sections.

In Scotland the bulk of the land is rough grazing. Out of a total area of 19 million acres only 4·6 million are under crops and permanent or temporary grass. 3 million of these 4·6 million acres are under crops—a much bigger proportion than in England. 1·4 million acres of this 3 million is temporary grass—also a much bigger proportion than in England.

As already pointed out about four-fifths of the entire country is under grass of some kind and so is growing food for live-stock. And more than half the crops grown on the rest of the land are also used for feeding animals.

The idea most people have of British agriculture growing food for direct consumption by human beings is all wrong. Its main concern is fodder for animals and far and away the most important kind of fodder is grass.

What are the chief features of these different grassland divisions?

The main rough grazing areas are on the mountains and heaths in the North of Scotland, north of England and Wales. Some parts of this country are so over-run with bracken, bilberry and bog that they are practically useless for feeding animals. Other parts grow poor grass which has not much food value. What small areas of rough grazing there are in the south of England, the dry and barren heaths and brecklands, are infested with rabbits.

These rough grazings are continually being changed by two processes. On the one hand, much of the rough land where sheep used to feed is now useless because of the bracken which has been allowed to cover it; on the other hand, the rough grazing area is continually being added to from the permanent grass area. The least good pastures in the permanent grass area are neglected and get rougher. Waterlogged fields in valley bottoms become overgrown with bulrushes. *Nardus* (mat grass) spreads over exposed hill pastures. On the whole these two processes tend to cancel each other out. The area which rough grazing loses by the first it gains from permanent grass by the second. In other words, the rough grazing area is slowly moving down the hillside.

Permanent grass is mainly found in the Midlands and Southern counties. It is relatively scarce in the dry eastern counties and in Scotland. Permanent grass is going through the same sort of process as rough grazing. Some pastures are lost to rough grazing but more are gained from land which used to be under crops and is now being put under grass. Permanent grassland is slipping from the lower hills into the plains, and from the west across to the east of England.

A larger area of pasture has meant a greater number of livestock. Grass is by far the largest crop fed to animals. We cut $6\frac{1}{2}$ million acres for hay (including seeds hay from temporary grass) and this is worth about £14 million a year. In addition to cut hay another 14 million acres provide animal food in the form of grazing. Assuming the value of grazing to be only a quarter as much as that of the hay fields, probably an underestimate, this would be worth £7-8 million. So that the value of hay and grass together is over £20 million a year. And as we shall see later there is more room for improvement in grass than in any other single crop. The position of temporary grass in relation to the arable rotation system is one of the most interesting problems of agriculture. Such grass can be made much more valuable as nutriment for animals than permanent pasture can ever be. In the old four-course rotation grass occupied one-quarter of the land. Under that system grass was quite subsidiary to other crops. To-day the area in temporary grass is tending to increase, partly because clovers restore nitrogen to the soil and partly because the grass smothers some of the weeds. When grass is ploughed up the fertility accumulated in the soil may be used for growing corn crops. The land is then sown with grass again and the cycle repeated. Perhaps this grass-land-arable farming will do for the 20th century what the four-course rotation did for the 19th.

The new emphasis on grassland farming is partly due to recent research into problems of soil fertility and partly to new types of grass and methods of grazing which increase the carrying capacity of pastures.

The problem of fertility is that of maintaining the productivity of the soil. Land is a capital asset which must be kept in running order. Land which has been untended or over-strained soon gives poor yields. Originally the way to keep land healthy was to fallow it every third year; later this result was achieved by rotations and the application of organic and inorganic manures. It is this fundamental necessity of maintaining the physical properties of the soil which largely determines what one can or cannot do in farming. Neglect of this law in the great fertile virgin lands of countries like the United States has brought many of their farmers into serious difficulties to-day. In Britain we have not lived on our capital to the same extent partly because of our system of mixed husbandry; partly because our climate did not produce soil erosion and partly because of our tradition that one must maintain the land " in good heart ".

The most recent results of modern research suggest that undue stress has been laid in the past on the rotation system and that physical properties of the soil can be maintained just as effectively, perhaps more so, by keeping the land under grass provided it is good grass. It has been noted that when a corn crop is sown after two or more years of well-managed grass, it is heavier than that grown in the usual rotation. Two or more crops in fact may be grown in succession before the land is put to grass again. This system brings the added advantage that it requires less manual labour than traditional arable farming. In view of the rising cost of labour this is an important factor in farming to-day. It is alleged that in certain areas the land is too light for satisfactory grass and will go derelict unless wheat and beet are subsidized. There is not sufficient evidence to show whether this is an important consideration or whether it only refers to a small acreage.

We may now consider the question of what constitutes well-managed grass which can yield as much nutritive matter as the roots, barley, seeds, wheat combination and to see what are the achievements of modern research in the matter of the production of more nourishing pastures.

Improvement and Management of Grass

It is important to note in the first place that grass is really as much a crop as anything else which grows in the soil and calls for as much attention as any other crop. It cannot be allowed just to grow by itself, as and how it pleases.

There are many varieties of grasses with varying degrees of usefulness, the differences between the various kinds are almost as important as the differences between the various corn or root crops. The question of seed selection is therefore one of first importance. Very careful research has been employed on seeds.

The type of grass also which is sown depends very much on the length of time for which the pasture is desired. It has further been noted that certain districts acquire special reputations for certain kinds of grass, and that attempts to breed grass in one country for use in another have not always been successful. Grasses are quite as fastidious to changes of climate as animals.

The breeding of grasses is hardly out of the experimental

stage, and we may look forward to great technical strides. Indeed, it is probable that the next generation will see revolutionary changes in grassland farming, in the use of new breeds or strains of grasses, and in the discovery of new and more scientific principles of grassland management. Already grasses have been developed which come into growth at different seasons, so that all-the-year-round grazing is almost practicable.

One of the most valuable results of research work has been on the question of manures. Grass stands as much in need of nourishment as any other crop. The choice of manure will vary according to the use to which the grass is to be put. For example, "manuring for mutton" with basic slag has greatly improved pastures in the North of England, and the introduction of wild white clover in Aberdeenshire has made "the fields in mid-winter as green as a billiard table". Yet many farmers still expect grass to grow by itself, and do not see that a little money spent on fertilizers saves a bill for winter feeding-stuffs.

The tractor has played an important part in modern grassland development. Without it it would never have been possible to consider breaking up some of our worst hill pastures. The amount of horse and man labour necessary would have put the cost out of all proportion to any reasonable return. With a tractor any land can be ploughed up cheaply and quickly.

By all these methods then, better seeds mixture, cheap mechanical cultivation, and scientific manuring, we are in a position to-day immensely to improve the value of our grasslands. We can get the pasture we desire, and regulate to some extent its seasons of growth. Because of new technique it pays to improve grassland on a scale which twenty years ago was inconceivable.

The value of grass as a feeding-stuff is also now better understood. Young grass is extremely rich in protein, the older it grows the more its food value (including starch content) declines. It is therefore better to graze a pasture frequently than to allow the grass to grow rank;

hence the practice of rotational grazing, that is to say, moving cattle from field to field. This, however, does not solve the difficulty that at one season the grass grows faster than they can eat it, whilst in winter there is practically no growth at all. As well as being grazed, grass has to be preserved for winter keep.

Methods of Preservation

There are three main methods of preserving grass; natural drying (haymaking), artificial drying, and the making of silage. The last of these is least in importance. It is a method of storing fodder in towers or pits, from which the air is excluded. It is really an elementary form of canning. Interest in silage was never great in this country, and is now on the wane.

The most general method of storing grass is, of course, haymaking. The criticisms of haymaking are that the grass is usually cut at its least valuable period, when it has grown up into rough stalks with a diminished feeding value and that a further part (often from a quarter to a half) of the feeding value is lost in the haymaking, largely due to the uncertainties of the weather. Were it not for the weather these objections might be met partly by improved methods such as earlier or more frequent cuttings, drying in frames or racks, and more careful carting and handling.

The most interesting innovation in grass preservation has been the discovery of the method of drying grass by artificial means. Hot gases from a furnace are passed over and through the grass which is placed on a fixed frame or on movable bands in machines. The advantage of artificial drying is that we can cut the grass when it is at its juiciest and best, and preserve the valuable qualities of this juicy young grass practically without loss. All forms of stock like and thrive on it. It makes a balanced food rich in protein and minerals and so may prove a substitute for imported concentrates.

There are technical and engineering problems yet to be solved and it is not possible to draw definite conclusions from the results so far achieved. One thing is certain, grass-drying demands more careful management of the pastures than haymaking, and it may be that it is this, more than the drying process itself, which is the important thing. It can never become a complete substitute for haymaking, because hay and grass perform distinct nutritive functions. It takes its place, however, as an important factor on the progressive improvement of the productivity of our grasslands.

State Policy

Until quite recently Governments have not taken any account of grass. They have been concerned only with stimulating arable farming by subsidizing wheat and beet, but there are indications that the State is becoming alive to the supreme importance of grass in our agricultural economy. A beginning was made by the Land Fertility Scheme of 1937 with subsidies for lime and basic slag. These subsidies reduce the cost of lime to the farmer by 50 per cent, and of basic slag by 25 per cent. During the first six months of the Scheme nearly 100,000 farmers made applications for grants amounting to about £600,000. Yet how far these subsidies will effect their purpose remains to be seen. Labour costs play an important part in the farmer's decision whether to lime or not to lime. Moreover, the selection of only these two fertilizers is open to criticism. The merit of the Scheme is that it has directed the attention of farmers in increasing degree to the possibilities of grassland improvement.

It may be argued that manuring merely touches the fringe of the problem, and that immense derelict areas should be ploughed up and resown. This consideration undoubtedly helped the Government to offer £2 per acre for the ploughing up of inferior grassland. How much further this policy should be carried has not yet been decided. It raises wider issues of investment in large improvement schemes. The statesman and economist have to weigh the alternatives and the cost of improvements which the technician has shown to be possible.

We are convinced that far more attention will have to be devoted to grass crop in future. It is a crop preeminently suited to the climate and labour conditions of the country. It is the principal feeding-stuff of our livestock. It is a crop which, when well managed, conserves fertility in the soil which can be used in time of emergency. It would be wise for the State to spend more liberally on research into strains of grasses and grassland management, and extend subsidies to other fertilizers than lime and basic slag.

CHAPTER V

GRAIN CROPS

Production

THE grain crops of the country have always filled a large place—possibly the first place—in the mind of the ordinary citizen when considering the land question. To him, the waving field of corn is the symbol of agriculture. What is not generally realized, however, is that the growing of corn has become decreasingly the be-all and end-all of farming in Great Britain. It is not grown for its own sake alone. It plays its part—an important one it is true—as one of a series of crops grown under a system of rotation. The farmer grows root crops to clean the land for corn; he grows corn to get straw, and he feeds cattle in order to use straw and roots and in order to get manure. Indeed, it may be said quite truly that the growing of corn as well as of the other crops of the land are parts of a system which is really the adjunct to our live-stock industry, which to-day is the greatest of all agricultural interests in this country.

The predominant grain crops are oats, wheat and barley. Of the oats, two-fifths are grown in Scotland whilst England grows over 90 per cent of the wheat and barley.

The total area under these crops in Great Britain in 1937 was just under 5,000,000 acres, compared with 7,000,000 acres in 1913. It is this loss of 2,000,000 acres which has bulked so largely in all discussions of the agricultural question. In the course of the contraction of our arable acreage, the driving force of circumstances has led to considerable changes in the geographical distribution of the areas devoted to certain types of crops. Much of the 2,000,000 acres lost to corn growing is marginal land on which it paid to grow cereals at the pre-war level of costs and prices but on which production would be unprofitable to-day. Farmers found it necessary to seek out only the more suitable land for such crops; thus wheat and barley, though still found to some extent in the Midland and Southern counties, have become concentrated mainly in the Eastern and drier parts of the country, Norfolk and Suffolk producing over a quarter of our barley. Oats remain fairly widely dispersed throughout the country. But the general position to-day is that cereal farming, as a dominant factor in agriculture, is now found only in parts of Eastern Scotland and the Eastern counties of England.

The main causes why so many acres have gone out of grain cultivation and others have steadily retreated to more advantageous land have been the relatively rising costs of production at home, of which wages form the largest item, and the competition of imported corn from overseas. The general level of agricultural wages is rising steadily and they are not likely to fall to any extent in the future. There have been, however, certain counteracting influences at work. Stimulated by the drive of rising costs and falling prices, farmers have been obliged to seek out compensating economies in all the processes of cultivation and harvesting, such as the substitution of machinery for manual labour wherever possible, the wiser use of fertilizers and the improvements in general farm organization. Indeed, but for this, the shrinkage of the corn acreage would have been still greater.

In the increased mechanization of farming, first in importance is the Tractor, of which there are now over forty thousand in use here. It has greatly reduced the cost of both man power and horse power and because of the increased pace of a tractor over the horse has made the farmer more independent of the weather. Second in importance has been the Combine-harvester, which reaps and threshes in one operation. The chief drawback to its successful use at first was that it left the straw standing, which had afterwards either to be burnt off or ploughed in. And the value of the straw is no insignificant proportion of the value of an acre of a grain crop. This difficulty was overcome by a machine which could reap the straw as well as the ear. However, as farms are laid out at present, the more familiar reaping and binding machines will continue to be used to a great extent, on probably more than half of our grain acreage. This way of harvesting has been made less expensive than it used to be by the use of a petrol-driven engine for threshing and by improvements in threshing machinery.

Probably the mechanization of farming has gone as far as conditions will permit in this country, having regard to the general lie of the land which we cannot alter, and to the lay-out of our farms in small fields which could only be altered slowly and at great expense.

Marketing and Utilization

Looking further afield for ways of increasing efficiency, we turn to the question of the marketing of corn. This, unlike the marketing of other agricultural products, evokes little criticism. Home grown wheat is sold mainly by sample and although this may not be altogether a satisfactory way of dealing, it is difficult to see any practicable alternative. Real grading as in Canada is not feasible when so little of the crop is bulked. The corn merchant's trade is a highly competitive business and is probably not unduly costly having regard to the services it performs.

In the case of barley, the sale-by-sample system has given occasion to farmers for complaint, owing to differences of opinion as to what constitutes a good malting sample. The marketing of oats is not of great importance, as most of this crop is kept on the farm for feeding to animals.

While the processes of producing and marketing cereals are all very similar, the uses to which they are put differ widely. Of home-grown wheat, about two thirds is milled into flour chiefly for biscuits and cakes, about a quarter is used for stock and poultry feeding and industrial purposes; the rest is held back for seed. In the case of barley, about one-half is used for malting and of the other half, a small amount enters the home; the rest is used for stock feeding. In the case of oats, more than ninety per cent is used for feeding animals. Altogether over sixty per cent of our total corn crops is used for animals. Yet we still think all corn is grown primarily for human food; and it still remains the principal consideration of statesmen when framing food defence measures. As a matter of fact, not more than about ten per cent of home grown wheat is used in normal times in the bread we eat. The flour made from it contains too much moisture and would make bread too heavy and dense. The practice accordingly is to mix about ten per cent of British wheat with imported wheat.

Imports

The broad facts about our corn imports are these. We buy from abroad seventy-five per cent of our total wheat requirements, forty-five per cent of our barley and eight per cent of our oats at a total cost of £30 to £40 millions. India, Russia and the United States, which used to send us large supplies, have dropped out, at any rate for the time being. Consequently we are more dependent on Canada, Australia and the Argentine who send us 80–90 per cent of our imports—meanwhile we are now the only important buyer in the world market, European demand having diminished. This has introduced a disturbing price instability and it may thus happen that even a slight increase over the normal world production of wheat may send the price down considerably with serious consequences to the British grower.

It is difficult to speculate as to the outlook for wheat in the great wheat-growing countries. In the beginning the farmer there ploughed in the rich virgin soils and grew crop after crop of wheat without regard to any rotational systems. With a high degree of mechanization, made possible by the lay-out of his farm, he was able to produce wheat in great abundance and at a cost with which the British farmer could never hope to compete.

But this persistent drain on the primitive fertility of the soil cannot continue indefinitely. The overseas farmer may —perhaps the process has already begun—be forced into methods of reinforcing the fertility of the land. And when he has to put the land out to fallow, to apply fertilizers and introduce live-stock and alternative crops his costs of production may increase and world wheat prices might naturally be expected to rise. On the other hand, we have to reckon with the progress of science and invention which should reduce costs still further. But whatever may be the course of events, the very real present-day fact is that for a number of years the world price of wheat has continued to fluctuate severely, and always in a downward direction with disastrous results to British farming. It was this which led the British Government to step in.

Cereals Policy

In 1931, the period of great trade depression and widespread unemployment, the Government decided to assist British wheat-growers and passed the Wheat Act which guaranteed to the farmer stated prices for his wheat in spite of any fluctuations of the world market. In 1937 another Act was passed giving help to growers of oats and barley. In May 1939 a plan to extend this assistance was put forward to apply retrospectively also to the crops for 1938. The additional anticipated cost for that year will be about £2,120,000 for oats and £800,000 for barley.

It has not been difficult to secure a generally sympathetic hearing. Bread is the staff of life. Wheat makes bread. Therefore wheat is the most essential food-stuff. It was also popularly supposed, though quite erroneously, that wheat was the corner-stone of British agriculture, and that arable cultivation increased employment. A measure to stimulate wheat, it was believed, would therefore feed the people, increase the number of workers on the land and so help in the solution of the general unemployment problem.

The principle of the wheat scheme was as follows. The farmer received a guaranteed price for his wheat, based on a standard price of 10/- per cwt. If the market price of wheat fell below this guaranteed price, the State made up the difference to the farmer. The actual amount of the guaranteed price varies with the home output; it falls as the home output rises. The figure quoted is paid on an output of 8,000,000 quarters or less (the figure in the original Act of 1931 was 6,000,000). For an output over 8,000,000 quarters there is a proportionate reduction in payments to the farmer. These payments are made to the farmer exclusively on the wheat he sells off the farm; but, in practice, only a very small proportion is retained by the farmer for his own use. It has also to be noted that the rate of the subsidy is governed by the average price of wheat in the market, not by the price at which an individual farmer sells. He gets the subsidy irrespective of the price for which he sells his wheat.

The subsidies are paid by the State out of funds raised from a duty on flour collected from the millers. This duty is imposed equally on flour made from home-grown and imported wheat, but as the home supply is a small proportion of the whole the subsidies, for all practical purposes, may be said to come almost entirely from the duty on imported wheat flour. In the last resort the burden of these subsidies is really borne by consumers in the form of dearer flour. The scheme operates on a large scale only when prices are low and wheat therefore abundant. It is estimated that for the year 1938-9 the wheat subsidy will total £9 million (an equivalent of roughly three farthings on the 4lb. loaf).

The benefits of this scheme to the farmer have been very substantial. In response, the production of wheat increased gradually from 1·25 to nearly 1·9 million acres between 1931 and 1935, although the greater part of this increase was at the expense of barley and oats, so that the net increase of arable was not so great. On the other hand, one of the effects of this increased wheat production has been a considerable fall (about £1 per ton) in the price of wheat straw. But as most straw is kept on the farm this loss passes largely unnoticed.

One of the criticisms of the Wheat Act is that it unduly favours a small number of arable districts in the Eastern and Southern parts of Britain where wheat growing is concentrated. The Acts of 1937 and the proposals made in 1939 have to some extent remedied this inequality for they extend the principle of price guarantee to oats and barley, but this guarantee is worked out on somewhat different lines from the Wheat guarantee. Oats and barley payments are based on the acreage under the crops, not on sales of the grain as in the case of wheat. Under the 1937 Act the subsidy was calculated on the basis of a yield of 6 cwt. per acre of oats. The 1939 proposals are based on a yield of 14 cwt. per acre. The standard price suggested is 8/- per cwt. as under the 1937 Act. Once the amount of the subsidy has been ascertained, namely the difference between the market price and the standard price, the farmer is paid that amount for each acre of oats grown, whether he sells it or not. For example, if the market price is 7/- per cwt., a farmer gets 1/- per cwt. Subsidy or 14/- per acre whether he actually grows 14 cwt. per acre or not. By the 1937 Act the grower of barley received a similar amount for each acre of barley grown but the subsidy depended on the price of oats and not on the price of barley. Under the new proposals (1939) brewers, distillers and other users of barley are to ensure a reasonable price to barley growers for a part of the crop. The Exchequer is to insure the risks attaching to the remainder.

These oats and barley subsidies are paid direct out of the Exchequer, unlike the wheat subsidy which is paid out of a levy on flour millers and largely passed on to the consumer. Payment was made retrospective to June 1938, the estimated cost being roughly £2,000,000 for oats, and £800,000 for barley. The maximum Exchequer liability in respect of the oats subsidy was estimated at about £4,500,000 in any one year and for barley about £1,250,000 in a year.

It should be noted that under the 1937 Act farmers were only allowed to claim a subsidy either under the Wheat

Scheme or the Oats and Barley Scheme, but not under both. Under the 1939 proposals farmers claiming under the Wheat Scheme may also claim under the Oats and Barley Scheme, though at a lower rate than those who claim for oats and barley exclusively. Oats growers (also claiming for wheat) may now get an oats subsidy on 6 cwt. per acre, with a maximum payment of £1 per acre. This applies retrospectively to the 1938 crop. For the 1938 crop barley growers will get 13/6 per acre. This is an interim expedient until the Exchequer and users of barley have worked out a common scheme of assistance to growers. The Wheat Acts have been in operation for five years and it is possible to draw some conclusions as to the effect of such legislation on the future of agriculture in its relation to the national welfare. These Acts were not designed, in the first place, as a measure of permanent protection to corn growing in this country, but for the purpose of ensuring to the farmers a price for their corn at a level roughly approximating to, but not above, the normal level of the world market. There was clearly a case for such a policy. But the scheme, beginning as a price insurance against ruin, is now operating as a plain subsidy which farmers are coming to expect as a matter of right. We are already seeing attempts to get the standard wheat price raised to 50/- per quarter on the plea that costs of production are rising and that unless State assistance is increased, more land will go out of wheat cultivation.

The danger of such appeals and of political pressure would, if successful, be that the State might be committed to a policy of maintaining, indefinitely, the present type and extent of arable farming, which, in fact, is not the most suited to British conditions. We must not shut ourselves off from the possible benefits of discoveries which may reduce prices and involve radical changes in our cropping systems. The price insurance scheme must be one which saves the farmer from being squeezed by a world slump in prices, not one which saves him from keeping pace with the steady growth of technical progress.

Against the plea of rising production costs may be set the increasing substitution of machinery for man power in all the processes of tillage which have been going on at a rapid pace in recent years. Actually there were in 1937 some 87,000 workers less in agriculture than in 1931 and to this extent the hopes of increasing rural employment built on the Wheat Act have been falsified. Of course, it may be said that without the subsidies the exodus of workers from the land would have been greater. But the fact that farmers are getting through their work every year with fewer men is not, in itself, a development to be deplored. It really points to a higher standard of efficiency (including the use of labour-saving devices) and it is to the development of this greater efficiency that we must look as the hope of British farming. Further economies might be effected by the amalgamation of farms into groups and the planning of their lay-out on more scientific lines, so as to permit of the more extensive use of machinery.

On general economic grounds, it would be unwise to give permanent and artificial encouragement to expanding wheat production in this country. Wheat can be grown far more cheaply overseas. It is pre-eminently a crop suited to large-scale farming methods which we cannot hope to attain. It is a commodity which enters largely into our overseas and inter-Imperial trade. The path of wisdom does not point in the direction of increasing the guaranteed price or acreage provided by the 1931 and 1937 Acts. In the light of all the circumstances, we would suggest that whilst retaining the principle of a price insurance scheme there should be a gradual reduction in the amount of State assistance. This might result in some decline of the corn-growing area of the country from its present extent, but there is no reason to suppose that the shrinkage would be so rapid as to cause undesirable dislocation. With the development of greater efficiency it should be possible to maintain quite a considerable acreage under grain, without the State having to fix a guaranteed price much in excess of the long-term "normal".

CHAPTER VI

ROOTS AND SUGAR POLICY

Root Crops

THE crops which go under the name of root crops are turnips and swedes; cabbage, kale, rape and other varieties of the cabbage family; mangold and sugar beet of the beet species; and the potato. In the plan of British farming the root crop performs two important functions. It provides winter food for livestock. The turnip and cabbage varieties and the mangolds are grown almost entirely for this purpose. The turnips and cabbages used for human consumption do not take up much more than 50,000 acres of the total 2,000,000 acres under roots in Great Britain. Certain by-products of the sugar beet, and surplus from the potato crop also contribute their share to animal feeding. This then may be considered the primary object of growing root crops. But they also play an important part in arable farming by cleaning the soil and preparing it for the growth of cereals.

As root crops have little or no competition to meet with from imports, it might have been expected that they would have shown greater steadiness in production than grain crops. Indeed in view of the great increase of the live-stock population of the country we might have looked for an increase of the acreage under roots. But the case has been quite otherwise. Leaving out potatoes, the total acreage under root crops has shown a steady decline in the past 25 years; and this has been particularly noticeable in the case of turnips and mangolds. The explanations of this decline have been, firstly, the more extensive use by farmers of imported feeding-stuffs, and secondly, the steadily rising costs in the production of root crops.

The chief factor in the increased costs of production has been the continuous rise in agricultural wages. Root crops require a very large amount of human labour in planting and harvesting, especially at harvest-time when mechanical methods, from the nature of the crops, are almost out of the question. A recent inquiry into the comparative labour requirements of roots and other crops showed that sugar beet, potatoes, mangolds and turnips called for about three times as much manual labour and twice as much horse labour per acre as cereals. Mangolds and turnips, with their comparatively low feeding value, have suffered the most severely from the increased labour costs and it is now doubtful if they can be grown profitably on any great scale.

Two serious consequences follow from this state of affairs. If the decline of these root crops—so essential in their cleansing action on the soil—continues the whole arable system will tend to become more and more unprofitable. And at the same time the increasing expense of growing roots will make it harder for farmers to show any profit on the production of fat-stock. Our root crops are in truth the weakest point in the structure of British farming. The State has done nothing about it directly. Indirectly, through the sugar beet subsidies, farmers have been induced to change over to a more profitable kind of root crop, and in this way the fall in the acreage under roots has been arrested to some extent.

An exception to the acreage decline in roots is to be noted in the case of rape, kale, cabbages and field vegetables in general. They require less attention than turnips and mangolds and the best of these crops can be sold for human consumption. They are also more suitably adapted for labour-saving methods, and are more likely to survive than turnips and mangolds.

Sugar Beet

The cultivation of the sugar beet is a comparatively young industry in this country. It had begun on a small scale before the war and was stimulated by the necessities of the war, but it was not until 1924 when the State decided to foster the sugar beet industry by substantial subsidies that it came to have an established place in British agriculture, and to form an important addition to British crops.

To the farmer the "tops" of the plant left on the field and the pulp residue from the sugar manufacturing process are excellent food for livestock. And it is a particularly good cleaning crop, its roots going deep into the soil. But it is a costly crop, calling for heavy expenditure on labour and fertilizers, and it would never have obtained a firm footing in this country without State assistance.

The Government were influenced by a variety of considerations in coming forward with offers of assistance to sugar beet. If it could be built up into a substantial industry, the State would at the same time be giving appreciable help to agriculture, promoting employment and making the country more self-supporting in the matter of its sugar supplies in time of war.

The subsidies were paid by the State to the sugar manufacturers on the amount of sugar produced by them. They were fixed on a diminishing scale extending over a period of ten years beginning with a grant of 19/6 per cwt. of sugar in 1924-27 and ending with 6/6 in the period of 1931-34. At the end of this period the position was to be reviewed.

There followed an enormous expansion of this industry. The area under beet in England and Wales rose from 22,000 acres in 1924 to 396,000 acres in 1934. The number of sugar factories grew from 3 to 18 and the home production of sugar increased from 24,000 tons in 1924 to 615,000 in 1934.

It was, however, a very costly business to the State. In the ten years the total sum paid in subsidies was £40 million. This was the sum received by the sugar manufacturers but it turned out that this was just about the equivalent of the sum paid by them to the beet growers for the raw material. In other words, the State paid for the raw material, and the price realised in the sugar market just covered the costs of manufacture and the profits.

A more serious matter was that, although both beet growers and manufacturers had improved their methods and effected economies in costs of production, hopes that the industry would be on a self-supporting basis by the end of the ten years were not fulfilled. What had happened in the meanwhile was that a great change had come over the world position of sugar. Sugar was being produced from the cane in other countries at prices with which no beet sugar industry could compete. Actually in 1930-1 £7–8 million was spent in this country in producing 8 million cwt. of sugar which we could have imported for £2·8 millions. The dilemma then in 1934 was either to abandon the sugar beet crop altogether or continue it with further State assistance. A committee set up by the Government recommended the abandonment of the experiment. The Government, however, decided to continue the subsidies and the Sugar Industry Re-organisation Act of 1935 was passed.

Under that Act no limitation was fixed as to the period of further assistance, but the subsidies were limited to an output of not more than 560,000 tons of sugar, the estimated product of 375,000 acres. The sugar factories were amalgamated into a body called the British Sugar Corporation, Ltd., with limitations on the dividends they could pay; and the whole industry was put under the supervision of a Sugar Commission. This Commission determines the amount of the subsidies, after taking account of the size of the crop, the contract price for the beet agreed between the Corporation and the growers, the Corporation's profits in the previous year, and the price of raw sugar.

This scheme involves at present an annual State subsidy of £5–6 millions. If, however, the costs of beet production should rise seriously in this country, in comparison with the costs of production overseas, and to such an extent as to threaten a decline in the acreage under sugar beet, we may expect urgent demands for increased subsidies

Before discussing further the position created by present State policy and the possible lines its direction should take in the future it is necessary to look more closely into the question of our imports of sugar.

Imports and Refining

We import about three-quarters of our total sugar requirements. The significant facts about these imports are their sources. Before the war half of our sugar came from Germany and Austria, beet growing countries; to-day nearly half comes from Cuba and St. Domingo and 40 per cent. from Australia, Mauritius, British West Indies and S. Africa, all countries where the sugar is produced from cane, and it was the sensational improvement in the productivity of sugar cane in these countries which brought about a great fall in the world price of sugar. Twenty-five years ago the price of raw sugar in London was about 12/– per cwt; in 1936 it fell to about 5/– per cwt.

The British Government, when they introduced their Scheme in 1924, did not appear to be fully aware of the changes which were taking place throughout the world in sugar production. Sugar bounties in the exporting countries may have contributed to the falling prices but the chief factor was the great improvement in methods of production from cane. The new sugar cane has cut the price of sugar by half and made any sugar beet industry permanently uneconomic.

As regards defence it is preferable and cheaper to safeguard ourselves by storing sugar.

Other problems arose in connection with sugar refining. Most of the sugar factories did some refining, chiefly in the off-season when their plant was idle. They could not, however, compete with the large factories which specialized exclusively on sugar refining. In 1928, these sugar refineries were able to secure from the State a protective tariff on refined sugar. Since then they have developed an extensive business of importing raw sugar, refining it and re-exporting it, and have engaged in a fierce competition with the sugar beet factories. This was a ruinous policy for all concerned and it was adjusted by an Industrial Agreement allocating refining quotas between the parties, the sugar factories being allowed to refine about 25 per cent. of the nation's annual sugar requirements.

Sugar Policy

Let us now consider what conclusions may be drawn from this sugar experiment as it affects British Agriculture.

The first and most important object of the scheme was to check the decline of the area under the plough and make arable farming more profitable. The decline in arable acreage, however, has continued even in the places where sugar beet was established. The best that can be said for the policy is that the decline has been less in these areas than in other parts. The reason why the decline has not been more effectively arrested is that sugar beet cultivation has taken the place, to a great extent, of other crops less profitable. The sugar beet crop had manifest attractions to the farmer. The fact that he grew the crop at a definite contract price with the sugar factories brought an element of security into his budget and provided him with ready cash. The second important result expected was a great stimulus to employment on the land. There were reasonable grounds for such expectations. Sugar beet is a crop requiring more labour than any other crop. What has actually been achieved is an increase in casual labour in the sugar beet districts whilst other parts of the country show a decline in casual labour since 1924. As regards regular labour, however, the sugar beet areas show a decline in the number of workers, though this decline is less pronounced than elsewhere. Taking agriculture as a whole, the subsidy has to some extent slowed down the decline in employment on the land but has not stopped it.

In view of the better prices now enjoyed by farmers for many other products of the land, under State protection, and the higher wages bill involved for sugar beet, the probabilities are that unless the subsidy is increased the acreage in sugar beet will tend to decline, and all hopes of increased employment on the land from that source will fade away. The question arises whether on national grounds this is a result to be greatly deplored.

The fact we have to face is that, in view of the technical improvements in the sugar-cane industry, the fall in the world price of sugar must be accepted as permanent, and we can rule out any probability in the future of beet sugar being able to compete with cane sugar on an economic basis. We have spent up to the present nearly £72 million in sugar subsidies and are pledged to spend further sums of £5 million or more a year to maintain the sugar industry on its present scale. On what grounds is the continuance of this policy justified?

Firstly it is said that sugar is heavily subsidised in other countries and it is unreasonable, therefore, that Great Britain alone among the nations should leave its domestic sugar production unprotected. But even if all other countries stopped their subsidies, we doubt if the position of British beet sugar would be materially improved. It would still be up against cheaply produced cane sugar.

It is said, however, that this imported sugar is the fruit of cheap native labour in the plantations, against which the workers of this country should be protected. This argument, however, would only be valid if we were prepared to see all trade between high-wage and low-wage countries disappear altogether. It is a sound principle of international trade that we should be ready to take from other countries the things they are relatively better fitted to produce.

The argument is sometimes used that the low world price of sugar is partly due to the increased supplies in this country, and that the consumer may thus be said to have benefited materially from the subsidies. According to this view, the abandonment of the subsidies and the passing out of the British industry might mean a rise in price of sugar to the consumer. There is, we think, some measure of truth in this argument, but not a great deal. The technical developments in cane sugar production have contributed far more than the British subsidies to reduce the price.

The case for security of sugar supplies in time of war and the danger of depending entirely on imports for an imported article of food is always strongly urged. But in view of the comparative ease with which sugar can be stored we are not inclined to attach much weight to this argument.

There is more force in the claim that the sugar subsidies have been of inestimable assistance to agriculture in just those parts of the Eastern counties which have suffered most severely from the trend of world conditions, and that but for the subsidies, coupled with the wheat subsidies, the plight of these areas would have been desperate. Without such assistance, it is argued, large tracts of these lands would have become derelict. In the circumstances of recent years, we have considerable sympathy with this point of view. The fertility of the soil is a national asset which should not be lightly thrown away. Undoubtedly the beet sugar subsidy has been a means of preserving this asset, and of maintaining the prosperity of the agricultural population in these areas.

But with all that can be said for the subsidy, it has been, as we have seen, an extremely expensive method of attaining its ends. We must, however, accept the position as we now find it. A Sugar Commission has been established with wide powers to direct the industry. The sugar manufacturing side has been re-organized. The farmers are relying on a continuance of assistance. It would not now be either practicable or reasonable to scrap the scheme. There are, however, some issues raised in its administration which call for comment.

It was laid down in the Sugar Act of 1935 that the subsidy was to be limited to the product of a beet acreage of not more than 375,000 acres. There are grounds, however, for suspecting that the Commission may tend to administer the scheme on a contract price between the Sugar Corporation and farmers, calculated on a basis sufficient to maintain that acreage. In other words, the maximum acreage may be treated as a minimum. The fact that, although the area under sugar beet had fallen in 1937 to 300,000 acres, the contract price for 1938 was raised from 36/– to 43/– per ton of beet suggests that this is the policy which is actually being pursued. If this line of policy is continued the scheme will be more expensive than ever to the State. The higher the contract price, the more costly will home produced sugar become and the greater the subsidy necessary to bridge the gap between home prices and world prices. At the same time, the likelihood is that the working production costs will rise in the future, in which case still higher subsidies will be necessary to protect the home product.

It is, we believe, in the opposite direction that our sugar policy should be evolved. We must consider agriculture as a whole. There was something to be said for the sugar scheme in its inception in view of the prevailing conditions in agriculture generally, and if there were no other ways of saving agriculture we should not recommend any reduction in the help it receives in respect of sugar. But we think there are many other ways in which farming may be given practical help by the State, as for example, measures to stimulate consumption of milk from which, we believe, agriculture would derive susbtantial benefit. We shall discuss these policies later, and we suggest that as progress is made with other measures of assistance the rate of subsidy to sugar should be gradually reduced. We do not think such a gradual reduction would be likely to involve any serious disturbance in agriculture, even in the sugar beet areas of the Eastern counties. A gradual withdrawal of support from sugar would stimulate farmers to make technical adjustments in the light of the latest scientific knowledge.

The Sugar Commission has power, if it wishes, to mould policy in this direction, but probably the most satisfactory way of carrying out modifications of policy on the lines suggested would be by fresh legislation defining more clearly the objectives which the Commission should pursue.

CHAPTER VII

FEEDING-STUFFS

IT has been pointed out in previous chapters how deeply the interests of British agriculture are bound up with the live-stock industry. It is necessary to emphasise this. Livestock farming is the main concern of agriculture in this country. About nine-tenths of our agricultural land is devoted to the growing of food for live-stock, and about one half of all the workers on the land are engaged one way or another, in this branch. In addition to this home production a large amount of feeding stuffs is imported from abroad. The problems arising from these two sources of supply profoundly affect the whole position of arable farming in this country and call for serious attention.

There are two governing considerations in the problem of live-stock feeding. The first is that animals require food all the year round whilst the food crops mature only at certain seasons. The second is that animals must be provided with a properly balanced diet which will keep them not merely in health but at a high productive capacity.

On the first question, it is important to note that winter feeds, whether roots, cereals or oil cake, are more costly to produce than summer grass. Some day, perhaps, science will point the way to the growing of grass abundantly in winter. But until that day comes we have to put up with all the consequences of the costliness of feeding animals in winter—in competition with countries where grass grows all the year round.

Next comes the problem of providing a balanced diet for animals with the right proportions of starch and protein. Animal foods range from the bulky foods of low nutritive value to the highly concentrated cakes and meals (cereals).

The aim of British arable farming, then, is not just to grow any kind of food, but as much of the right kind as it can do economically. Thus we grow most of the bulky foods, grass, hay, straw, roots and potatoes, some of the cereals used for feeding, and also, of course, milk fed to young stock. But we import much of the grain and cake or cake ingredients.

The importance of the various feeding stuffs has varied from time to time according to changes in their respective costs of production. Over a lengthy period there may be a considerable change over from one kind of feeding stuff to another. The amount of roots and cereals, and therefore of straw, produced in this country is very much less than 30 years ago. On the other hand the acreage under grass has risen considerably. And as the costs of production of grass and hay continue to fall relatively to those of cereals and roots, grass will more and more tend to increase in favour as a feeding stuff, and grasslands to extend over ever widening areas. Grass and hay may not be perfect substitutes for grain and straw and roots in the diet of cattle, but scientific research has shown that they possess very high nutritive properties. From the point of view of animal feeding, therefore, the change-over from arable to grass cultivation, or a greater emphasis on grass in the rotation system, is not a calamity. At worst it may force us to buy from abroad slightly more winter feed, presumably cheaper than we could have produced it at home. At best, we shall so extend our grazing season and our crops of hay and ensilage (and perhaps grass for drying) as to be less dependent on imports than before.

When we come down to the problems of the individual farmer who is both producer and consumer of feeding stuffs, we see that, whilst to some extent his choice depends on the situation of his farm and its soil, the primary consideration with him will always be the cost of growing his own feeding-stuffs compared with the cost of buying them. His aim is to feed his live-stock on the lowest priced foods consistent with adequate nourishment. When, however, he is faced with the question whether he should change over from one crop to another which costs less to produce, it does not follow that the difference in costs is the simplest answer to his problems.

Farming is such a complex of interlocking enterprises that it is not always easy to abandon the cultivation of a single crop—however unprofitable it may be.

In the end the successful farmer is the one who can most readily adapt his farming to the changing trends in world conditions. The outstanding fact is that the cost of imported feeding-stuffs to-day is very much less than the cost of growing them at home. This is partly counteracted by greater efficiency in grass production and the technique of grass drying. The farmer may become more of a manu-facturer, importing his raw material in the shape of feeding-stuffs and converting them on his farm into meat, milk and eggs. It is of the utmost importance, therefore, to British agriculture to have some idea of how the costs of home produced feeds are going to compare in future with the cost of imported feeds.

Imports

Of all the food consumed by live-stock, apart from fresh grass, we grow just over half and import the remainder. Most of the imports are in the form of raw material—mainly wheat, barley and maize—which are manufactured into feeding-stuffs in this country. The feeding-stuffs which arrive here already manufactured, such as maize meal, wheat offals and cake, represented in 1937 £13·4 million (out of a total of £45 million). This latter was just about the value of the feeding-stuffs (excluding grass) grown at home.

The largest single item is wheat offals—bran, middlings, etc.,—the by-products of the flour milling industry. The mills take practically all the home-grown and the imported wheat; and their annual output varies little. This means that the price the farmer pays for his offals depends almost entirely on the strength of the farmers' demand. The more popular these foods become the dearer they will be. If, for any reason, wheat should become dearer and the costs of production of offals go up, the increased price is reflected much more in the price of bread and flour than in the price of feeding-stuffs made from wheat.

The amount of barley used for live-stock, in the form of meal, is comparatively small and of our total requirements less than one-half comes from abroad, chiefly the U.S.A. and Canada. Ten years ago, Germany took over half the world's imports of barley; to-day only one fifth, leaving Britain as the biggest buyer of barley in the world markets. Barley prices may therefore be expected to remain low.

Maize, which is ground into meal or otherwise prepared before being fed to animals, is the only cereal imported on a large scale which cannot be grown commercially at home. Our principal source of supply is the Argentine. The price of maize seems to follow very closely the price of barley down to the smallest monthly variations. Maize meal and barley meal can obviously be substituted the one for the other.

Oil-cake and oil-seed meal represent an annual expenditure on feeding-stuffs to farmers of some £10 million a year, equal to their purchases of wheat offals. Oil-cake is made from seeds (cotton seed, linseed, etc.) or nuts or beans (chiefly soya) from which the oil has been pressed out.

The oil (used in margarine and soap) is really a more valuable product than the cake. We import ready-manufactured cake to the extent of about one-third of our total cake requirements. The sources of supplies of cake in the world are widely distributed and these should be a safeguard against any sudden shortage in one country or disturbance of supplies from any cause in another.

Our fiscal policy operates curiously in the case of some of these imported feeding-stuffs. It taxes foreign linseed, soya-bean cake and meal, cereal meals and offals, taking

E

from the farmer with one hand nearly £700,000 a year and with the other hand giving back part of it through the cattle subsidy. Reviewing our importations of feeding-stuffs as a whole, the most striking fact is the great diversity of the sources of supply. If for any reason the production in one country runs short this may be balanced by increases from other countries, and a constant supply for our own needs every year may therefore be generally expected. Another point is that most European countries cannot easily make themselves self-sufficient in such feeding-stuffs as maize, oil-cake and oil-seeds; so that international trade in feeding-stuffs has suffered less than the trade in other agricultural products.

Conclusions

We are now in a position to review the whole problem of the feeding of Britain's live-stock. The task is to keep the animals fed on a balanced ration all the year round at the lowest possible cost. There are three main sources of supply, British grassland, British arable land and over-seas countries. The general trend has been for the feeding-stuffs produced on grassland and those produced overseas to become cheaper than those produced on our arable land. Accordingly, there has been an expansion in the area under grass, a rise in the amount of imports of feeding-stuffs and a steady decline in the arable acreage in this country.

From all this it would appear that if arable farming is to be protected, the only feasible method of doing this is by assisting the live-stock industry. The worst way of going about this would be the imposing of severe tariffs on imported feeding-stuffs. What we need is a policy designed to encourage the production of those types of feeding stuffs in which we enjoy a natural advantage. The trend over many years now shows with increasing clearness that the fodder crops which we can best produce are grass crops.

We have already stressed the inadequacy of our

traditional farming system as the basis for our great live-stock industry. There is first the steadily growing cost of working the ordinary four-course rotation in which the chief factor is the labour bill. Second in importance is the experimental work with grasses which is only in its infancy but which within a few years may be expected to bring about a considerable lengthening of the grazing season and therefore a large addition to our home supply of feeding-stuffs. The third important factor which has come into prominence in the last few years is the alternative feeds available—new types of cake, such as ground nut cake, and the still more interesting development of grass drying. This may provide a home-made concentrate of high protein content and enormously increase the demand for the produce of our pastures. There is good reason to believe that other crops, besides grass, can be preserved for food by the method of artificial drying if more efficient drying machinery is evolved.

It may be contended by some that the line of policy in regard to feeding-stuffs which we have indicated above will tend to the disappearance of arable farming from the land. We are convinced, however, that a greater increase of grass production will not necessarily have this effect. The modern tendency, as we have seen in Chapter V, is not in the direction of permanent pastures, but towards increasing the amount of land laid down to temporary grass in the rotation system. Arable farming will not disappear but it may change its character.

It may also be noted here that grass, hay, and concentrated feeding-stuffs play by far the greatest part in the ration of dairy cows—90 per cent according to the report of a recent enquiry. The sheep population is also mainly fed on grass. Actually it is only the beef cattle industry—and only half of that—which uses a large quantity of roots and straw.

In conclusion we would emphasize again that British agriculture is mainly concerned with live-stock farming, and the live-stock farmer needs more than anything else to be able to obtain good quality feeding-stuffs at reasonable prices. Accordingly, it should be a principal feature of any agricultural policy to facilitate the provision of these from the most appropriate sources. The aim should be to grow at home the crops which can most economically be produced and import the remainder. It is possible that research may discover arable crops other than those now grown, which may go far to replace imported feeding-stuffs at lower prices per food unit. The tendency in farming practice is towards more grass crops and fewer corn and root crops. The State's policy of subsidizing sugar-beet and wheat has impeded this process of adjustment. We believe that more substantial encouragement should be given to improved grass production. This is essential if Britain is to avoid becoming too dependent on imported feeding-stuffs. Finally, it seems unfortunate to tax imported feeding-stuffs such as linseed and soya beans, which we cannot grow on a commercial scale. We advocate the reduction and where practicable the abolition of these duties.

CHAPTER VIII

POTATOES AND HOPS

Potatoes

THE potato, which furnishes so large an amount of the food of mankind, is grown almost everywhere. Every farm has its potato patch, large or small, but certain districts make a speciality of it, particularly Lincolnshire and the Lothians. Scotland also has made a feature of the production of seed potatoes which are in great favour because of their comparative freedom from disease. The potato is extremely subject to disease, particularly blight (the cause of the Irish famine in 1844) and wart-disease. These diseases are, however, kept well under control to-day.

The Earlies or new potatoes are grown in a few special districts and generally command a high price, but until main-crop potatoes are ready, they have to compete with considerable imports from the Channel Islands and Spain. These Earlies, however, do not amount to much more than 10 per cent of the total home crop.

There are two main problems of the potato industry, the first is the great instability of prices from year to year, and even in the same season. This arises generally from deficiencies of the crop owing to disease and bad weather. The fluctuations in the prices of potatoes are probably greater than in those in any other agricultural product. For example, in 1931–2, a season of an unusually low home crop, the price rose to £10–£12 per ton; whilst in 1929 a particularly heavy crop brought the price down to £2 10s. and £3 10s. per ton. An interesting point here is that the public demand is not much affected by price changes. In a bad year, when a supply is short it takes a large rise in price to make the public eat less potatoes.

The main problem of the industry is the disposal of surplus stocks in years of abundant harvest when the public demand has been more than satisfied. One way of disposing of surplus is in the manufacture of starch, of which the potato contains large quantities. The second method is the making of alcohol for various industrial uses from the potato's starchy matter. A third and perhaps more practicable method of dealing with surplus is the drying of potatoes for stock-feeding. The Potato Marketing Board has recently established a factory at Wisbech for this purpose. Surplus potatoes can be most conveniently disposed of by feeding directly to stock, mostly to pigs.

A point of importance in connection with the marketing of potatoes is that it is a bulky crop and transport costs over great distances to markets may be very high. This leads to large variations in prices in different parts of the country.

The Potato Marketing Scheme

It is clear from what has been said that one of the main concerns of the potato industry is the problem of marketing. There was in the past little or no organization or system about that market. It lacked adequate information about the many complex factors affecting prices. Yet the potato is a crop eminently suitable for organized marketing. Imports are not a serious factor except in the case of Earlies. Consequently, potato growers took advantage of the 1933 Marketing Act to set up a Potato Marketing Board.

The main object of the Board was to regulate the supply of potatoes going on to the market in order to prevent great price fluctuations. Supply is controlled in three ways: firstly by rigorous control of imports; secondly, by a system of acreage quotas, and fines on producers for increases in acreages above their quotas; and thirdly, by regulating the supply allowed on the market by what are known as "riddle regulations".

Control of imports will generally only come into play when a short crop in this country coincides with more abundant crops abroad. Such imports relieve the scarcity of bad years. They cannot affect the home producer adversely in the long run, because he can always depend on high prices in scarcity seasons. At the same time, if the scheme is to safeguard the home producer's prices, imports must be regulated. Otherwise any attempt on the part of the home producer to raise prices by curtailing production would bring imports rushing in to fill the gap. Control is effected through licences to import allotted by the Board of Trade to individual potato importers.

The second method of control of supplies—by quotas and fines—is effected as follows: A Basic Acreage Committee of the Board allocates to each producer so many acres which may be either his acreage in 1933, his average acreage from 1931 to 1933, or, for small producers (under 7 acres) his highest acreage in the three years 1931 to 1933. For every acre used by the grower in excess of this allotment he must pay a non-recurrent fine of £5 to the Board. A similar fine is also payable by every new entrant into the industry. This fine may not be prohibitive but it is a fairly stiff deterrent to increased production.

The third method of controlling supplies—"riddle regulations"—has reference to the system used in sorting out the different kinds of potatoes—seed potatoes, potatoes used for home consumption, and those used for stock-feeding—by passing them through a riddle or sieve with meshes of different diameters. The riddle provides a simple device for regulating the supply. It is only necessary to forbid the sale of potatoes smaller than a certain diameter to control the quantity of the potatoes coming on to the market. The Marketing Board in practice has to rely on the general experience of its members. There have been complaints that one effect of the "riddle regulations" is to discriminate between different potato producing districts, penalizing any district in which the natural size of the potato is small.

The distribution of potatoes is largely controlled by the Board. All sales have to be effected through authorized merchants. Sales on commission are prohibited. Local committees of merchants have been formed under the title of "Marketing Co-ordination Committees" for the purpose of checking price-cutting among merchants. They have no statutory powers but they can report merchants to the Board with a view to having their authorizations taken away.

This Scheme has undoubtedly reduced the fluctuations in potato prices but there has not yet been time to judge the Scheme in its entirety. We must await the results of a number of years before a fair judgment can be made. But in any case, whether the Scheme at the moment is working well or not, it seems to us unwise to entrust such extensive powers to a Board composed exclusively of producers' representatives. This raises a general principle of policy which applies equally to the other Marketing Boards. In order to guarantee that the various Marketing Schemes will function truly in the public interest we believe that they should be controlled by nominated bodies, responsible not to producers but to Parliament. We have set forth the reasons for this proposal at some length in our chapter on Milk Marketing. Similar considerations apply in the case of potatoes. A nominated Board or Commission could more safely be entrusted with the regulation of imports, the fixing of prices, the control of acreage and the authorization of merchants than could a producers' body. It would be in a position to initiate adequate experiments in providing potatoes at reduced prices, thereby stimulating consumption and providing some outlet for surplus supplies.

Hops

Hops, with an acreage of only 18,460 acres in 1938 confined mainly to Kent and Sussex in the south, Herefordshire and Worcestershire in the west, is a crop of minor importance in British agriculture.

This crop is particularly interesting as the Hop Marketing

Scheme is the first and most complete of all the Schemes under the Marketing Acts of 1931 and 1933.

It is the most monopolistic of all the Schemes. All hops are sold through the Board which can destroy any surplus. The price has been stabilised at £9 per cwt for five years, recently raised to £9 10s. for another term by an agreement with the Brewers' Society. This is about the average of the years 1927–1933, which was £9 13s. The Board may be thought to have used its monopoly powers to raise prices for growers to a greater degree than was justified as, with freedom from competition, growers need not fear losses and so do not have to average good with bad seasons.

Monopoly is useless without adequate control of supply, and this the Board achieved by limiting production by means of basic quotas. The effect of this is to create monopoly values entirely for those who were growing hops at the time the quotas were fixed. The right to grow hops has thus become a saleable commodity, and basic quotas are bought and sold at the rate of about £12 per cwt. Taking a 200 acre farm with about 20 acres of established hops on it, and in possession of a Hops Quota appropriate to that acreage, the effect of the monopoly has been to increase the value of the farm by something approaching £2,000. In other words if such a farm were rented at £200 per annum, the rent would have risen to £300.

No better example could be found of the creation of values by means of artificial scarcity. Hop growers who had temporarily gone into fruit before the year on which the quotas were based have been deprived, without notice or compensation, of the opportunity to grow hops. Moreover, there is no reason why the increased land values resulting from the monopoly should go into the pockets of either a small class of growers or their landlords rather than into the Exchequer. Incidentally the brewers were brought under the influence of the monopoly by the establishment of a strict import quota.

Foreign hops may be imported up to a strictly limited aggregate quantity only. So long as that limit is not passed, an individual brewer may import the foreign hops he needs, but in the event of the limit being exceeded in any year, there will come into operation a strict control of imports notwithstanding any deficiency in the quality of the English crop.

When the Board commenced its operations, it was clear that the powers conferred upon it were too wide to be left to be operated by the producers including, as they did at first, the power to determine the price to be charged to the consumers. After considerable negotiations an agreement was arrived at between the Board and the Brewers' Society under which a Joint Committee was established consisting of three Independent Members nominated by the Minister of Agriculture, together with representatives of the producers and the brewers. All major questions of marketing, where producers come into contact with their customers, are determined by this Joint Committee without which it is difficult to see how the Hops Marketing Scheme could have been made workable.

The Hops Scheme provides a powerful argument for the transformation of producers' Boards into nominated bodies representative of the public interest. We would like to see the Hops Board reconstituted in this way. We believe that if this were done it would ensure the gradual removal of the opportunity for abuse which exists under the scheme were agreement not secured, as at present, with the Brewers' Society. The import quota should be revised so that new entrants may be allowed into the hop-growing industry.

We have in both these instances, the Potato Board and the Hops Board, an illustration of the danger of granting excessive powers to producers' bodies which have no responsibility to the public or to farming as a whole.

CHAPTER IX

OTHER VEGETABLES

THE demand for vegetables has steadily expanded in recent years. This is due mainly to a growing appreciation of their nutritive value—especially in vitamins—and also to the general rise in wages which has enabled more people to buy vegetables than formerly.

This growth in the public demand has occasioned the rapid increase in vegetable output which has been one of the features of British Agriculture. The total acreage—peas, cabbage, brussels-sprouts, beans, carrots, cauliflower and broccoli—rose from 126,517 acres in 1922 to 226,815 acres in 1936. The old established vegetable areas have expanded some 50 to 70 per cent, but the increase has been mainly in areas like East Anglia where vegetables were previously little grown.

Production

Three main types of grower compete—the small market gardener, the large market gardener and the general farmer.

The chief handicap of the small grower—besides his rent, which is usually high—is that all his work is done by hand, usually by himself and family. He has many other disadvantages compared with larger growers, especially in the matter of fertilizers. His animal stock being small, he has difficulty in getting the necessary farmyard manure. Artificial fertilizers such as soot or shoddy are expensive and are not a perfect substitute for farmyard or horse manure. The larger market gardener is also able to afford more machinery.

In recent years, growers on a large scale have come into the business, specialising in growing vegetables and nothing else and using mechanical devices to the utmost. There are farms on which 2,000 acres are being cultivated on these lines. These large-scale growers are able to buy seeds and fertilizers in bulk more cheaply than the smallholder. And they are more ready and able to take advantage of the latest technical developments of cultivation and of pest control. Their wages bill is high—about £15 per acre a year. The large specialist vegetable farms do not yet, however, supply most of our vegetables though their numbers are constantly recruited from general farmers.

The biggest expansion has been on mixed farms, since horticulture brought a new source of income when other farm enterprises were becoming less profitable. What began as a temporary expedient to tide over bad times, soon became a permanent profitable venture on a large scale. To-day vegetable growing fits well into the routine of the mixed arable farm and has proved a beneficial addition to the rotation system. It also enables the farmer to make use of his labour throughout the year, providing work at times when otherwise operations would be slack.

The mixed farmer enjoys other advantages, namely the ability to keep his land in good heart cheaply with farmyard manure. Nor is he obliged to grow vegetables on the same soil every year. As already explained, he has steam cultivators, tractors, ploughs, hoes, etc.,—which he can use at times when they are not wanted for other crops. All this enables him to reduce costs and has been one of the main factors in the expansion of vegetable growing. Concentration so far has been on those vegetables which are most easily grown—carrots, peas, etc.,—but there is every reason to expect an increased production of the finer and more expensive varieties such as lettuce, celery and asparagus, so far produced mainly by large and small specialist growers.

The final advantage enjoyed by the mixed farmer is that he can, if necessary, use any surplus vegetables to feed his live-stock.

Marketing

The smallholder usually disposes of his produce to dealers on the farm, or in the local market, and by auction in larger markets. The larger growers usually employ commission agents who operate in the big wholesale markets. Some growers sell their crops whilst they are in the ground and are thus freed of the trouble and cost of picking and marketing. Others aided by motor transport trade direct with hotels, institutions and retail shops, so cutting out the cost of the middleman. But in practice this has not been entirely satisfactory as the producer is not always in a position to offer his customer sufficient variety. For this reason, hotels and shopkeepers who have to study the requirements of their customers, prefer the wholesale market which offers a wider choice.

The problem of efficient marketing is thus not a simple one, and the present position is far from satisfactory as is seen in the great fluctuations in day to day prices for a single commodity. In the course of an enquiry at Evesham it was found that prices of runner beans jumped from 1/– to 4/– per pot in four days during the height of the season; and peas fell from 4/– to 1/9. These fluctuations were mainly due to each producer's ignorance of what others were doing. There were also many price variations even on the same day, all indicating a lack of co-ordination.

Alternative outlets for at least a part of the crop might be found in canning. Canning has made remarkable strides in the last fifteen years, especially in the case of peas. The canning of other vegetables has made less headway although there are signs that certain kinds of canned vegetables are becoming popular as ways are found of reducing the price. Usually the canning firms make contracts with growers, in advance of cropping, for some of their supplies, and wait to buy the remainder when the crop is marketed. Farmers however still look upon canning only as a useful stand-by and prefer to sell for direct consumption. Canning may ease marketing problems: it cannot solve them.

One obvious improvement in marketing would be in better grading and packing. The grading arrangements of the producers in this country compare very badly with those of foreign supplies which are most carefully selected and packed before being exported. There is for certain vegetables a National Mark Scheme (a system of grading organised by the Ministry of Agriculture) but it has not made much progress among the small growers who feel that the terms of grading are too exacting.

Packing matters quite as much as grading. The bulk of a vegetable crop is not consumed locally but is sent long distances to the big centres. Boxes are the best form of container as they keep the produce better and are easy to handle. But their cost falls heavily on the small grower. It would be a great advantage if growers would set up some form of district packing as fruit growers are beginning to do.

The storage of perishable vegetables has not been fully explored. If successful it would solve many marketing problems by lengthening the season of vegetables otherwise only available for a few weeks. In conjunction with canning this would expand consumption.

Consumption

There is every reason to suppose that the demand for vegetables will go on expanding as the knowledge of their food value increases. Vegetables contain, more than most foods, those essential mineral salts and vitamins without which any diet is deficient. An advertising campaign, setting out their merits, should be a feature in any campaign to improve the nation's health and welfare.

It is not possible to give exact figures of consumption, but it has been estimated that the average annual consumption per head rose between 1909–13 and 1934 from about 60 lbs. to 98 lbs. Cabbages and onions head this increase and celery is at the bottom. Two factors determine public taste. One is price, and the other is the length of season for which the vegetables are available. Cabbages and onions may be had all the year round and are cheap. Celery is neither available all the year round nor cheap. The problem of increasing popular demand for seasonal vegetables can probably only be met, as already indicated, by storage and canning.

Imports are not as considerable as in other branches consisting chiefly of out of season vegetables. Growers have been given tariff protection which has undoubtedly expanded the production of certain vegetables. Care should be taken not to encourage by excessive duties the production of such things as tomatoes which for lack of sun can only be grown in greenhouses when outdoor produce can be imported cheaply.

We cannot look to further restriction of imports for future expansion of vegetable production. That expansion will rest on the growth of consumers' demands, which, in turn, will be stimulated by reductions in price and by improvements in the quality and presentation of the produce. General improvement in grading and packing is therefore essential. At the same time, in order to stimulate a rather more rapid increase in consumption, desirable on health grounds, we urge that by education, advertisement and propaganda, the nutritive value of vegetables as an essential food, like milk and fruit, should be brought more forcibly to the public notice.

CHAPTER X

FRUIT

THE peculiarity of fruit from the agricultural point of view is that once it has been planted it remains in possession of the land for a number of years, and cannot therefore enter into any arable rotation as vegetables can. This characteristic cuts it off from other farm enterprises.

The consumption of fruit has increased enormously in the last 30 years. This is partly due to a recognition of its valuable health protecting qualities, stimulated by effective publicity such as the "Eat More Fruit" campaign of a few years ago; but mainly to there being imports from overseas at all seasons and at fairly steady prices. Fruit was formerly a seasonal luxury; now it has become an all-the-year habit. Improvement in quality and presentation for sale also helped to increase demand. In these respects the high standard of imported fruit stimulated British growers. As a result of these developments the quantity and quality of fruit supplies are more consistent.

Because of the technical knowledge and organisation required fruit-growing must be undertaken by specialist producers. This has involved a shift in the areas of production since the new specialist producers have found it less costly to plant orchards on land unencumbered with old fruit-trees. The south-east of England has developed, and the west, mainly cider-apple orchards, has declined. Soft fruits have also shown a tendency to migrate.

Technical Developments in Production

In fruit production, as in all the other branches of agriculture, science has made great contributions. One of the most important improvements being in the quality of plants which now grow true to type and are healthier.

Progress is being made by genetics in the control of the breeding of new varieties of fruits, with a view to securing earlier or later ripening and improving their flavour. But, except in the case of apples, there are still many technical problems unsolved. What is particularly wanted, at present, is a greater study and appreciation of the importance of quality in fruit and a more widespread planting of the finest known varieties.

We need more information about the suitability of soil, manuring and cultivation. But soil varies so much from district to district that nothing short of a national survey —an expensive business—would provide accurate data for growers as a whole. Increased knowledge of the effect of manures on fruit trees indicates the necessity of segregating crops according to their chemical requirements; e.g. as potash is a limiting factor in the growth of apple trees and nitrogen for stone fruits they should not be grown together, nor should vegetables (nitrogen lovers) be grown in or pigs run in apple orchards.

The most baffling problem in fruit growing is the control of diseases and pests. Disease is more serious than it was 30 years ago. It developed greatly during the last war and in the 1919–20 boom when diseased stocks were indiscriminately planted, and disease-carrying plants imported.

The only effective ways of combating these plagues are the production of healthy stock, and spraying. Raspberry and blackcurrant yields are 50 and 45 per cent higher respectively than 15 years ago through improved stock. With orchard-trees, even the healthiest stocks are attacked by pests, and high-power spraying apparatus is necessary. Its purchase is expensive, costing from £100 to £200 (without the tractor to draw it). This expense handicaps small growers and prevents their spraying adequately.

But the most scientific orchard management may be nullified by bad weather. More should be done to provide farmers with meteorological information, detailed in its local application. If growers knew a few hours in advance of a coming weather freak, they could take appropriate measures. There is also need for research on the effect of winds and draughts on orchard temperature, as well as the effect of orchard heaters against late frosts.

All these modern developments in the technique of fruit growing involve considerable capital outlay. To establish a commercial orchard requires £100 per acre before the trees come into bearing. And the running costs are also high; they may exceed £100 per acre per annum. On this scale, two years' bad crops would put a small-holder with little capital practically out of business. Any great expansion in the fruit industry would appear therefore to rest with men of considerable financial resources.

Marketing

The disposal of fruit does not present difficult problems. Fruit may be used for jam, canning, fruit-juice, and cider, as well as for direct consumption.

At one time jam-making was the principal outlet for soft fruits. In the last 14 years, however, conditions have changed and jam is to an increasing extent being made from imported pulp.

When the British canning industry came into existence our growers had high hopes of it and in 1932 the home output of canned fruit was about half-a-million cwt.; but since then the industry has marked time. The chief difficulty is the competition of imported canned fruit such as Californian peaches (subject to 15 per cent import duty) and (duty free) pineapples, chiefly from British Malaya. Canners also complain of the quality of our fruit (especially plums). The outlook for canned fruit is less favourable than for canned vegetables.

Fruit-juice manufacture is a recent innovation. Drinks mixed with fruit-juice have long been popular in other countries; and milk bars, with their mixed milk and fruit-juice drinks, are popularising a pleasant habit here. Fruit-juice has one great advantage over jam-making or canning. Any healthy fruit may be used without regard to size, shape or quality.

The marketing of fruit for direct consumption is similar to that of vegetable marketing. The most noteworthy feature in recent years has been the growth of co-operation for grading and marketing among apple growers. In some counties eight or a dozen growers, with 30–50 acres of orchard each, share a packing station and market all their produce under a joint name. A system of central grading and packing stations, combined with storage, offers the best opportunity of competing successfully with imports, unless fruit farming is run in large units of 500 acres or more.

Imports

Most of the fruit we eat comes from abroad, but less than one third (by value) of these imports could be grown out of doors here. To encourage fruit growing, tariffs were imposed on imports from foreign countries in 1932, and caused a drop from £48 million in 1927–9 to £40 million. Empire fruit comes in duty free, and this preference has increased the Empire's share in our total fruit trade from 27·8 per cent in 1929–31 to 65 per cent in 1936.

It may seem at first that these imports are still too large and that further protection should be given to the British fruit grower. But in fact only a small proportion of imports are in competition with the home producer. Imports rise or fall according as the yields of the home crops are low or abundant. Fruit imports come in mostly during our off-season, and so provide a continuity of supply.

These results have been obtained through *specific* duties, which are heaviest during the season of low home prices, and partly from a gradual change in the sources of supply; and partly by the agreements made at the Imperial Fruit Growers' Conference to restrict shipments during our main-crop season. Supplies are therefore more evenly distributed, prices rise less in the off-season, and the public benefit. To this extent, the import duties have benefited home growers. It may be said that the duties on cherries, currants and strawberries cover too long a period, beginning to operate long before the home products are marketed. This safeguards the early market with its high prices for the home producer, but has the effect of confining the public demand to a short season of a few weeks.

Consumption

The yearly per head consumption of fruit has increased by 36 per cent since 1908. This increase has been greatest in tropical fruits (oranges and bananas)—from 27 lbs per head in 1908 to 49 lbs in 1936; in orchard fruit it was from 30·3 lbs to 36·5 lbs; but in soft fruits there has been a slight decline from 5·5 lbs to 3 lbs per head.

The variations in these figures arise mainly from the fact that new areas overseas have been planted up with orchard and tropical fruit; our imports have more than doubled and prices have fallen considerably. By contrast no new sources of supply of soft fruits have developed.

Another reason for increased consumption is the lengthening of the fruit season so that of certain fruits there is a continuous supply all the year round. For instance people may not eat more than 3 apples a week but if the season is extended from 8 to 12 months, total consumption rises.

Demand also increased owing to the rise in real wages during the last 30 years, which brought fruit within the means of many classes who could hardly afford any before. Some interesting facts were revealed by an analysis of family budgets made by Sir John Orr. Taking six income groups, he found that expenditure on fruit ranged from 2½d. per head per week in the lowest income group to 20d. in the highest income group. Fruit consumption is unlikely to increase substantially until fruit prices fall within reach of the income groups which at present buy relatively little.

Home-grown fruits are very cheap in their season, but the season, except in the case of apples, is a very short one, in some cases only a few weeks. This difficulty might be overcome by breeding new varieties which ripened earlier or later, or by successful storage. Unless the season can be lengthened in either of these ways there is not much hope for expansion in the consumption of home-grown fruit, except apples.

Future Prospects

As already noted, owing to the need for scientific knowledge and organisation, fruit growing in this country is passing more and more from general farmers into the hands of specialists, though the relative proportion varies in different areas. Many of these specialists (mainly large scale growers) have come from non-agricultural vocations—retired Colonial officials, business-men, ex-public schoolboys—and they have brought to the business of fruit growing standards of technical knowledge and efficiency rare in other branches. They have improved marketing by more attractive methods of presentation, by recognition of the importance of continuity of supply, and improvement in quality.

Yet all the developments in the technique of fruit production have not as yet led to any great expansion in output. This is especially so in the case of soft fruits—and of cherries, plums and pears. The determining factor in their case is the consumers' demand which has hitherto been limited to the short season of these fruits when prices are low. The remedy is not a further limitation of imports, for these are already negligible. The only hope for increasing demand lies in some lengthening of the season whether by storage or canning. Storage has not yet proved very practicable and the canning industry is up against much cheaper imported canned peaches and pineapples. The outlook for any great expansion of these fruits cannot therefore be considered bright.

The only home-grown fruit with really favourable

prospects is the apple. It is a cheap fruit and is now available all the year round. Through the new technique of storing apples, it is becoming possible to be self-sufficient for eight or nine months in the year. Our growers can thus win a share in the market previously served by overseas producers.

Apart from apple growing, there seems little immediate likelihood of an expansion of the home-fruit industry, although this does not mean that the public demand for fruit will stand still. That demand, as we have seen, is steadily increasing for all those fruits which are both cheap and continually in season. And from the point of view of national health, it is unquestionably desirable to stimulate greater consumption in fruit of all kinds whether home-grown or imported.

From the point of view of British Agriculture as a whole, fruit production is not a serious factor in its fortunes. It is becoming increasingly the business of specialist-producers and does not greatly matter to the majority of farmers. Fruit growing, even more than vegetable growing, must remain inevitably one of the minor enterprises of farming. In view of this we cannot advocate any special assistance being given as part of a national agricultural policy, though no doubt direct encouragement to fruit consumption would be included in any comprehensive policy of nutrition.

PART THREE

LIVE-STOCK PRODUCTS

CHAPTER XI

CATTLE

THE live-stock industry presents a great diversity of circumstances. Each division—cattle, sheep, pigs, and poultry—has its own peculiar structure and problems.

The production of meat is one of the outstanding branches of our agricultural system. Taken as a whole, live-stock accounts for about one-third of the total annual output of British agriculture. For the year 1935–6 the estimated total value of our agricultural output was £245 millions. Of this £87,180,000 represented the value of live-stock, i.e. cattle and calves £35,900,000; sheep and lambs £20,740,000; pigs £24,240,000; poultry (meat) £6,300,000. In addition our meat requirements necessitate imports to the annual value of some £70–80 millions.

Beef Production

There are two chief divisions of the cattle industry; the breeding-and-rearing and the feeding-sections, each carried on mainly by separate groups of producers working in different parts of the country, and with divergent interests as to price. But this specialized beef-production does not account for all our home beef supplies; we have to add a considerable contribution made by cows which have finished their time in the dairy industry, representing some 40% of the beef supplies, and a small quantity of veal, mostly of the unwanted male calves of dairy cattle.

Breeding-and-rearing is largely carried on in the remoter parts of the country where land is cheap and access to markets difficult. It is the larger of the two sections of the industry. The animal takes, on the average, about two years to rear whereas he is fattened for only six months. The number of animals in the hands of the rearers at any one time is therefore about four times the number in the hands of feeders. The importance of the breeding-section is further enhanced by the fact that the choice of breeding-stock mainly determines the ultimate quality of the progeny. Here there is much room for improvement. Too large a proportion of such progeny is bred from cows selected mainly for their milking capacity, and not for their beef-production record. Many calves are bred solely to get the cow into milk, the pure dairy farmer not being interested in the calves at all as their value is small compared with that of milk. This is especially the case in remote districts where the Milk Marketing Scheme has now made milk-selling profitable.

There is a general concensus of opinion that as a result, except in Scotland, the quality of home-produced beef has been declining seriously. To some extent the standard of our stock has been maintained by the store cattle imported from Ireland where the quality has notably improved in recent years through the earlier adoption of measures to license bulls and eliminate scrub animals. On the whole the breeding side is conducted in a far more haphazard, indiscriminating and uninformed way than the feeding side. This is a principal reason for the frequent lack of quality in British meat or rather, what is worse, for the extraordinary unevenness of its quality.

The feeding-section falls into two parts; summer fattening which depends mainly on grazing, and winter fattening mainly on arable crops. The most important centre of the grass feeding-section is the East Midlands but it is carried on to some extent in all parts of the country. In the grass-feeding system the animals remain the greater part of the time in the fields, and housing is only needed for the backward or sick.

Formerly the winter feeding of cattle in "yards" consisted of roots and straw, but sugar-beet pulp has come increasingly into favour. The centre of winter feeding is in the arable counties of East Anglia where the manure which the cattle tread is an essential part of the farming system, mainly because both the soil and the rainfall are light. This method of cattle fattening goes on even if, apart from the manure it produces, it is wholly unprofitable, because the arable farmer has no substitute for it. If he abandoned winter feeding he would have to abandon his whole system and in some cases the land might go derelict. There is, it is true, a steady but slight turnover to dairying and fruit farming even in the very centre of the winter feeding districts. But the necessity for animal manure remains, and since it can only be obtained to a limited extent from pigs, the yard feeding of cattle still continues.

The two systems of feeding dovetail into one another very conveniently to give us a fairly regular supply of beef throughout the year. Almost all the grass-fed cattle are sold between June and December, and winter fed beasts between January and May. The two halves of the feeding industry are nearly equal in size. This is important from the point of view of any legislation, for it means that the disappearance of either one or the other would create a serious disturbance in the whole structure of British beef production. The yard-feeders, owing to heavier labour requirements have experienced the greater difficulties recently, and it must be put to the credit of the sugar-beet subsidy that it has indirectly given material assistance to yard-feeders and saved them from being forced out of business. Farmers recently have finished their beasts at a much younger age than thirty years ago, largely in response to a demand for leaner meat and smaller joints.

Marketing

The marketing of cattle is done in two principal ways, either on the farm to a travelling dealer or in a market. The "on farm" sales are much fewer than formerly. In the market, the farmer may trade by private treaty either with dealers or butchers, but the common method is to buy and sell by auction. The auction may be described as the keystone of the whole marketing system, for it establishes a market price which forms the basis of all trading by private treaty. The auction markets are very diverse in character. They may be owned by a chartered corporation having a statutory monopoly within a 7-mile radius, by the municipality, by a private person, by a firm of auctioneers or by a limited company. It is certain that there are too many markets. Their number and diversity are legacies from the times when men walked to market and drove their animals in front of them. So we find all over England small market towns with about 20 miles between them inappropriate to an age of motors. A movement towards larger and fewer markets is noticeable. An example is Midland Marts Ltd. at Banbury which draws stock from more than half the counties. Large auction markets benefit farmers by removing the danger of "rings".

Besides the methods of selling animals by their liveweight, there is an alternative method of selling, by deadweight, which was introduced in London in 1930 and has since been operating in some half-dozen provincial centres. Under this system the farmer informs a grader—an official of the Ministry of Agriculture—at the City Market, that he contemplates sending a consignment of cattle. The grader then gets quotations from the wholesale dealers, (according to the various grades), which are passed on to the farmer. If the farmer accepts the prices he sends the cattle direct to the abattoir; the carcases are graded by the official grader and the farmer receives the prices quoted, auctioneers and middlemen being dispensed with.

Though this scheme has received much official encouragement it has not made much headway with farmers; less than 3 per cent of the cattle slaughtered being sold on this basis.

Another scheme of sale and wholesale distribution of meat advocated is the farmer-slaughter-house scheme. Most animals are bought in the country and slaughtered in the towns. It is claimed that animals lose condition in transit and should be slaughtered in the producing areas and transported to the towns as dead meat. The only outstanding success in this type of trade has been the Aberdeen trade with London, a highly developed trade in the best class of beef.

Apart from such special cases, probably the present system of slaughtering in the consuming areas is the most satisfactory. But it is capable of many improvements. The one-man private slaughter-house is mostly found in the villages and small towns where the butcher does the killing and sells the meat in his own shop. In the large towns, this system is rapidly disappearing and is being replaced by larger abattoirs where more beasts are handled, the various jobs connected with slaughtering specialised and certain benefits of mass production obtained. It is, of course, applicable only to large towns and we must not forget that a large proportion of the population lives in villages and small towns. How far slaughtering should be centralized is a question of a balance of cost and advantage to which no general answer is possible. Such evidence as is available suggests that in Britain the advantages of centralized slaughtering have yet to be demonstrated. Even if the centralized slaughter-house did its work more efficiently it would not be able to compete effectively with the present system in the small towns if the quantity of animals passing through it was small. The State is encouraging experiments to see the results.

The last link in the chain of distribution is the retail butcher. To-day he is more of a meat purveyor, who does not kill his own beasts as the old butcher did, but buys carcases or more frequently fore-or-hind-quarters and sometimes ready-cut joints. This is a development of the imported trade in frozen and chilled meat, most of which arrives in this country in the form of fore-or-hind-quarters. The retailing of meat is not inefficient apart from the unsolved problem of displaying to the consumer the quality of the article sold, especially in the case of home produced beef where lack of reliability in quality from day to day weakens our competitive power with standardised chilled imported meat.

State Policy

From a national point of view, the central problem of the cattle industry is how to compete successfully against the produce of our Dominions and of the Argentine. Owing to the importance of meat imports, the industry is peculiarly sensitive to the state of world trade. The severe fall in beef prices was specially acute in the autumn of 1932 and emergency steps were taken to restrict imports.

At the Ottawa Imperial Conference certain restrictions of imports were arranged but mainly with the object of giving Empire produce a preference over that of the Argentine. The danger to the home farmer of excessive imports from Australia was provided against by Australia agreeing to limit shipments to not more than 10 per cent above the "Ottawa year". But so serious was the situation in November 1932 that agreements were made with the South Americans that their imports should be reduced by 10 per cent, and this was followed in 1934 by other arrangements with Empire countries to limit their shipments (chiefly frozen beef from Australia and New Zealand). Since then improved methods of *chilling* have begun to alter the situation, imports of chilled beef from the Empire being five times greater in 1937 than in 1933.

These restrictions helped to save farmers from catastrophe though they did not restore profitability to the beef industry. Restriction of imports kept up the price of imported beef but it should be noted that the price of home beef continued to drop till 1935. The feeder in particular was hit. When the feeder buys stores he assumes that the prices of fat stock will still be round about the current level five months later when his beasts are finished and ready to sell; and since his raw material, the store, represents 75–80 per cent of the cost of the finished beast he loses heavily on a falling market.

Accordingly a system of subsidies was introduced in 1934, as a temporary measure, to avert a collapse. It totalled £3-4 millions per annum. In 1937 a long term policy came into operation. This provides an annual subsidy not exceeding £5 millions in any one year to be administered by a Livestock Commission. This Subsidy Scheme gave a rate of 5/– per cwt on live home-bred cattle ("ordinary") and 7/6 per cwt for better ("quality") cattle. The subsidies for imported animals were respectively 2/6 and 5/–. The higher subsidies for home-bred animals were intended to protect the British rearers against the Irish.

The superiority of Irish cattle is shown by the fact that in the first half year, three-fifths of the imported animals reached the "quality" standard compared with only two-fifths of the home-bred. In the same period 84 per cent of all the animals receiving subsidy in Scotland obtained the "quality" subsidy, in England it was only about 40 per cent, and in Wales less than 20 per cent. The figures for the year ended March 31, 1939, show an improvement since the inauguration of the scheme. In Scotland of all the animals certified 87.6 per cent obtained the quality subsidy; in England 63.1 per cent and in Wales 49.4 per cent.

The policy of assisting the industry by subsidies instead of further import restrictions was determined partly by the importance of our trade with the Argentine, partly by a desire to avoid raising prices to consumers, but also partly because of recognition that there are limits to which the restriction of imports can help the British farmer. This is due to the limited extent to which imported and home produced meat compete. They tend to have separate markets. The poor who usually buy the cheaper qualities eat mostly cow-beef or cheap imported meat; whilst the middle classes and the rich are the chief buyers of prime British beef. In consequence a restriction of imports has a much greater effect on the price of the imported meat than on the home product. Thus, after the beginning of import restriction, the price of imported beef ceased to fall whilst the price of home produced beef went on falling. This factor also operated with the bacon quota.

As an emergency policy, a strong case can be made out for a subsidy. But as a long term policy it is more difficult to justify. The purpose of the subsidy was not to guarantee a minimum price, as in the case of the wheat subsidy, for it is paid irrespective of price fluctuations. Moreover, it is only one of the many forms of State assistance which beef producers enjoy. They have import restriction agreements, and a tariff on imported beef and veal; winter feeders profit substantially from the sugar beet subsidy and graziers from the lime and basic slag subsidy. The cattle subsidy is large, likely to be expensive in relation to results, and it is doubtful whether it will achieve its avowed intention of preventing or at any rate retarding the contraction of the industry. British producers are at a natural disadvantage with producers on the cheap land and rich pastures of Australia and the Argentine. These disadvantages are likely to increase in the near future, for it is now becoming commercially practicable for Australia to send chilled meat to this country which will substantially raise the quality and competitive power of beef imports as a whole. Nor can the expansion of beef production be demanded on nutritional grounds as with milk, vegetables etc. for though certain income groups do not eat enough, yet as a nation our consumption meets health requirements.

If, as we hope, milk consumption increases, there will inevitably be a larger supply of low quality cow-beef. Lastly domestic beef being largely eaten by the well-to-do a permanent heavy subsidy becomes difficult to justify.

The main justification for a specialized beef industry is that it should produce the best quality meat commanding a high price. Farmers should reduce their output of the poorer grade beasts.

Since then, the subsidy itself is not a particularly appropriate instrument for helping to put the industry on a competitive footing, payments should be gradually reduced and put on a sliding-scale designed to operate only during periods of especially low prices, while proceeding to develop such forms of assistance as will tend to improve the quality, and hence the competitive power, of British beef.

Already numerous measures have been initiated. In Scotland since 1912 a scheme has been in operation, whereby premiums are given to the purchasers of bulls passed by Government inspectors as of "premium" quality (and certified free from tuberculosis). The Irish Departments go further than this and purchase high-class expensive bulls for loan or re-sale to pedigree breeders whose herds are already good enough to be improved by the best type of bull.

In England and Wales the premium bull scheme has never achieved significant results. Actually during the past few years less than 1,500 per annum qualified for the subsidy out of a total of 80,000 bulls. A more all-embracing measure was the Licensing of Bulls Act which came into operation in 1934, after which date all bulls on reaching he age of ten months have to be licensed. But the standard, besides varying from area to area, has had to be flexible; a too rigorous standard might have precipitated a bull shortage. Indeed, whilst eliminating the worst scrub bulls it does very little to encourage the production of really first class sires.

But from a national standpoint it is impossible as a long term policy to justify large subsidies to preserve the status quo, i.e., for beef, much of which is of mediocre quality, and which could be produced better and cheaper overseas— since then do not adequately stimulate improvement in quality. The only beef which stands a chance of competing with imported beef is that of the highest grade, in the production of which our farmers are unequalled; of the poor quality stuff the dairy industry will provide more than enough. Our policy should aim not at subsidizing a heterogeneous beef industry indefinitely, but at fostering a rapid improvement in quality. Indeed in the long run it may be better, even from the farmers' point of view to

F

prefer a policy which will put the industry in a position to produce an article that suffers little from foreign competition, for such a policy will command a wider measure of assent among non-agricultural sections.

What is needed to accelerate improvement in breeding? Education as well as co-ordinated and improved administration are the principal needs. At present the Departments of Agriculture have the main responsibility for the improvement of Livestock, but the Development Commission and the Agricultural Research Council are also concerned. The agricultural colleges and the Institute of Genetics come into the picture, so do the Milk Marketing Boards and the Welsh Dragon scheme; finally the more recently created Livestock Commission has the duty of improving the livestock of the country.

Thus a dozen or more different methods of raising the quality of cattle are in operation and others might be suggested: they cannot all be the best.

In these circumstances a conference for the interested parties might bring about greater co-ordination of effort and stimulate an educational campaign. In the meantime the County licensing system under the 1934 Act should be replaced by a more uniform and reliable one and the standard for licenses should be raised as rapidly as the necessary numbers of bulls in the country will permit, so that in a few years all the bulls will reach the standard now required of premium bulls.

CHAPTER XII

SHEEP

THE sheep industry resembles the cattle industry in its main outline with the same divisions into breeding and feeding-sections, the latter being sub-divided into grass-feeding and roots-feeding. There are, however, some important differences between cattle and sheep.

The length of life of the sheep before it passes into consumption is much shorter, and is steadily being reduced, for two reasons. Firstly, lamb is becoming more popular than mutton. This change has been very marked in the last ten years. 1924 lamb imports approximately equalled those of mutton: now they are nearly three times as great. In the home supply, out of 11 million lambs born in a year about 6 million are slaughtered as lamb, about 2½ million go into the breeding flock and eventually reach the market as old ewe mutton, and about 2½ million are slaughtered as mutton. Secondly, owing to the fall in wool prices, wool is now treated as a by-product of mutton rather than as a valuable commodity. This has affected the type of sheep bred—wool types being displaced by crossbreds, or mutton types.

Sheep-breeding is fairly widely distributed over the whole country but is most important in the Border Counties and Wales with concentrations in Kent and the Lothians. The breeding section of the industry centres largely in the Border Countries, although there is a fairly wide distribution of sheep breeding over the whole country, and generally speaking the store trade is far more local than in the case of cattle.

As already remarked there are two systems of feeding sheep. The first is associated with the use of sheep on arable land for maintaining the fertility of the soil. The sheep are folded on a field of roots which they eat, their manure making the soil hold moisture whilst their treading has a consolidating effect especially on light and porous soils. But the method of folding on turnips and corage crops is costly in the labour needed for moving hurdles, pulping turnips and extra attention at lambing time. With a long period of low prices for barley, it is not surprising that winter-feeding of sheep combined with barley production in the same district became unprofitable and declined. Since 1912, the ewe population in arable sheep counties has declined by 43·9 per cent, though in grass counties the sheep population increased by 17·8 per cent in the same period. The season of 1938 showed that the chalk land and wold districts—where arable sheep farming is mostly carried on—were among the most distressed areas in present day British farming.

It may be noted here that, with the decline of the number of sheep in arable counties, there has been a proportionate decline in the acreage under turnips and swedes. On the other hand, where farmers have gone in for vegetable growing, sheep are used for eating up unsaleable crops of cabbage and other roots.

In Southern Scotland and the North of England sheep breeding on mixed arable farms is universal. The ewes are wintered on grass supplemented with roots, and on the lower ground a proportion of lambs are sold fat before June. Later in the year the remainder are sold by auction either fat or as stores for winter feeding on roots. In favourable climates from the Moray Firth to Devon ewes lambs from January onwards and all the lambs must be sold fat early to be profitable. But the bulk of the lamb output is from grass fed lamb from June to October.

Arable and grassland systems of sheep farming are not necessarily opposed and there should be room to develop a system combining the advantages of both, based on a more widespread use of temporary pasture. Alternate husbandry of this kind may account for the increased number of sheep in the Lowland arable districts of Scotland.

Marketing

The Marketing of sheep is very similar to that of cattle. The Auction is the principal medium, the only difference being that sheep, by reason of their small size and large number, are auctioned in groups. The grading and dead-weight method of sale has also been encouraged in the case of sheep but again has not met with much response, though mutton and lamb are easier to grade in carcase than beef. The simplest grading system is by weight, sex, and age. But the most important factor, "goodness" is not easy to define. The Ministry of Agriculture runs a scheme of quality grades—"selected", "prime", etc. But the definition of these qualities are inevitably so vague that grading in these terms is not entirely satisfactory.

Hitherto marketing problems have not worried the sheep industry because until lately it has not had to face such adversities as beef production. Though prices fell in 1931–32 they then rose steadily until 1937. In other words, the crisis was much shorter-lived than for most agricultural commodities. In 1938, however, the situation became so acute that the Government intervened in 1939 with a price insurance scheme, involving a standard rate of 10d. per lb. dead weight. In some cases this should yield a profit and to that extent is more than an insurance scheme to prevent serious loss by putting a bottom to the market. It has been estimated that on certain broad assumptions the cost to the Exchequer of deficiency payments in 1938, had the scheme then been in operation, would have been about £2,500,000: and in the six years 1933–1938 might have averaged £900,000 a year.

Imports

Mutton and lamb like beef are, of course, faced with large imports, 58 per cent of our supplies coming from abroad, mainly from Australia and New Zealand. There was some increase in 1930—but it was checked by agreements with South American countries and the Dominions. The aim now is to maintain total prices at about the 1934 level and to adjust quantities imported to changes in British output.

The relative prosperity until 1938 of the British sheep industry is not to be explained, however, by these import restrictions. It is partly explained by the shift of public taste from beef to mutton and more especially lamb, but mainly by the superior quality of British mutton and lamb over imports. For this advantage there are two reasons. Since the value of wool has dwindled the primary object in sheep-farming has been the meat production. Sheep farmers have no dairy industry with dual purpose cattle to bother them and do not have their market spoiled, as in the case of beef producers, by a quantity of mediocre meat produced as a by-product. In the second place, imported lamb and mutton has come from Australia and New Zealand in a frozen state.

It is of the utmost importance, therefore, that British sheep farmers should not rest content with their present standards of production. Two lines of advance are possible: one is to improve the general level of breeding; the other to organize an attack on disease.

There is considerable chaos in sheep-breeding as almost every county has its own special breed, some varieties being confined to a few parishes. Pedigree breeders are inclined to give more attention to breeding distinctive "points" than to producing a good quality meat animal. What is wanted to-day is standardization of the more serviceable types. The quality of sheep hinges upon the quality of the *grass*-ewe and the ram she is crossed with and by her capacity to produce early maturing lambs, her fertility and her resistance to disease. Fertility is of special importance to sheep farmers because the depreciation of the ewe constitutes about a third of the cost of lamb production.

Disease adds substantially to costs. There are two aggravating causes, one is over-stocking on grass, the other is malnutrition arising from the lime and phosphate deficiency of most of our upland pastures. Research work on sheep disease seems to have been more successful than on cattle disease. But much remains to be done into the causes of lamb mortality which is about 10 per cent in England and Wales.

Breeds could be improved, the incidence of disease reduced, and fertility increased,—with such improvements the industry should, with some form of protection whether by price insurance or otherwise, be able to meet any increased competition from overseas.

Until recently there was no demand on the part of sheep farmers for special assistance and the industry has shown a tendency to expand. It is a branch of farming in which some expansion would be appropriate since it uses comparatively little labour and so will be less likely to suffer from rising wages. Moreover sheep farming is becoming increasingly divorced from arable farming and stands to gain from technical improvements in grassland management. It has also enjoyed indirect assistance through the lime and basic slag subsidies, and other Government encouragement to pasture improvements.

We would oppose a subsidy to sheep for the same reasons as we oppose subsidies to the cattle industry. But we would support any adequate measure designed to assist the improvement of quality. We also recognize that for sheep farming, which has to compete against such a large volume of imports, something may become desirable to steady prices in periods of severe depression.

CHAPTER XIII

PIGS

THE Pig industry, as with cattle and sheep, is divided into breeding and feeding sections. The pig lives chiefly on imported food so that feeding costs vary little as between districts and there is no striking geographical concentration of the industry.

The chief characteristics of the pig are that it matures within a shorter period than any other domestic animal, i.e. in an average of about nine months. It has also greater powers of reproduction, having about ten piglings to a litter and often two litters a year. This rapid turnover of the pig population is a governing factor in the industry.

The breeding side suffers from defects similar to those already noted in the case of cattle and sheep. There is the same lack of attention to breeding for performance; little breeding of clearly defined types for pork and for bacon; the same indiscriminate use of poor quality breeding stock. The only rational explanation of the numerous and, in some cases, fantastic breeds of pigs still to be found is that they were partly adapted to local meat requirements, and partly developed to please fanciers' tastes. A contributory factor to these various troubles may be that breeding is in the hands of smallholders, many of whom have not the knowledge or resources to produce a better type of animal.

Pig fattening is in the hands of four main classes; dairy farmers who use pigs to consume the by-products of milk manufacturing; ordinary mixed farmers and market gardeners who fatten pigs as a sideline, generally in some corner of the farm and use them to some extent as scavengers; mixed farmers who run a serious pig enterprise on commercial lines; and specialist pig farmers who produce little else. The first of these types is of little importance in this country, and is becoming of even less importance since the collapse of the farm cheese and butter industries under the Milk Marketing Scheme. This explains one difficulty of establishing a large bacon industry in this country. To compete successfully against Denmark where dairying is organized for the conversion of milk into butter, and skimmed milk for feeding to pigs would require a lengthy, expensive reorganization of our dairy industry which is now organized mainly to produce milk for sale as milk.

Most of the pigs in this country are produced on mixed farms. The question whether the business is to succeed depends in the main on the number of pigs per sow which can be brought to maturity, and the cost of management and feeding. In a litter of ten pigs probably not more than seven survive to be marketed. Survival depends largely on health, housing and general management. Most of the pigs are reared in old-fashioned sties or in all kinds of miscellaneous buildings. The "in-and-out" sty with its usual accompaniment of filth still houses a large proportion of pigs. There is a certain amount of purely open-air breeding and feeding but the exercise involved in such methods retards rapid fattening. The "Danish" type of pig house, where the pigs, living in a warm atmosphere, require less food, has attained some popularity here during the last few years.

Disease in a great many forms is a serious economic factor in the industry. The almost universal presence of rats where pigs are kept probably occasions much disease. The important factor in efficient production is the maintenance of general health so that the pigs may use their food to the best advantage and put on weight quickly. This demands constant observation and intelligent management and this is where the employment of skilled pig-men can play an important part. Probably one of the best ways of reducing costs in the pig industry would be to attract a higher class of worker by raising the wages of pig-men.

Feeding-stuffs constitute 70–80 per cent of the cost of producing a pig. To some extent pigs are fed on kitchen refuse and unsaleable crops of potatoes, etc., but the greater part of the pigs' food is bought by the farmer, in particular barley and maize meal, wheat offals, and fish meal. Farmers could, with advantage, feed more milk to pigs.

The Pig Cycle

There is a peculiar phenomenon in the industry known as the "pig cycle". All the statistics of the industry show a remarkably regular cyclical fluctuation within a period of about four years. It affects the pig population, output, the price of all the commodities involved in the industry, and profits. About the nature and causes of this cycle there has been a great deal of discussion and many factors are still obscure. But it runs somewhat on these lines. Pigs fetch good prices, therefore farmers go into pigs, therefore pig prices fall, therefore farmers go out of pigs, therefore pig prices rise, therefore farmers go into pigs, and so the cycle is repeated. It is equally remarkable that feeding-stuff prices follow an opposite course to that of the pig price cycle, being high when the price of pigs is low and vice versa. This is partly because when the price of pigs is high, pig population and output are low: hence the demand for feeding stuffs will be below normal.

Why should this cycle be four years? Probably what happens is this. At the bottom of the pig production cycle, when pigs are profitable, farmers decide to breed sows, and this results in a high pig population in two years' time. Then at the peak of the population cycle when farmers are incurring losses they get rid of a greater number of sows than usual; this again takes about two years to complete.

This four-year pig cycle exercises in many respects a decisive influence on the course of the industry.

The Marketing Scheme: Import Regulation

The pig industry, then on the downward phase of the cycle, was very badly hit by the 1930 slump. At the beginning of 1932 all pig prices had reached unprecedently low levels and producers were faced with a crisis. The Government set up a Commission to draw up a re-organization scheme. The Commission's aims were to increase very largely production of British pigs at the expense of foreign pigs (mostly Danish) and to eliminate the pig cycle. The Commission proposed two weapons: the Contract and the Quota.

The import situation was briefly this. In 1930 we were importing 85 per cent of our bacon and ham and 50 per cent of our pork. At the same time there was a rapid increase in production in Denmark, representing the peak of their pig cycle, which resulted in a great increase in exports to this country, bringing down prices. During 1932 the situation threatened to become more acute and the Government decided on a policy of import restriction. They arranged for a reduction of imports by 15 per cent, and in 1933 for a further reduction by 16 per cent. For 1934 and subsequent years after the probable home and Empire supplies had been estimated quotas were allotted to foreign countries, the object being to stabilize bacon supplies at about 10,670,000 cwts.

The intention of the bacon import restrictions was to reduce seasonal and cyclical fluctuations in price and to eliminate the difference in price between British and Danish bacon. Danish prices rose, but British prices did not (apart from the normal pig cycle rise in 1936). The reason for this is that imported and home bacon often differ widely in grade and quality. Danish bacon has established a high reputation for consistently good quality, and when supplies of it are short, the housewife does not easily turn over to the generally inferior British quality. She will frequently be more willing to pay a higher price rather than give up her Danish. As a result of quotas or import restrictions in 1934 we paid more money to the Danes for considerably less bacon than in 1933, which by no means displeased the Danes ! Actually the Danes would prefer this quota policy to be continued. The Boards did not foresee this and went about the business of re-organizing home production. The Bacon Quota forced the British consumer not only to subsidize the home bacon producer but also to subsidize two groups of overseas farmers, i.e. the Danish and other producers of bacon (who got a higher price) and also the overseas growers of the feeding stuffs which our farmers had to import for their bacon pigs.

The Contract System

Three Boards were set up: the Pigs Board for producers: the Bacon Board for curers: and the Bacon Development Board whose function was to regulate the whole industry with a view to improving technique both in production and in marketing.

The main business of the Pigs and Bacon Boards was to secure a guaranteed minimum price to bacon pig producers. It was sought to achieve this by contracts between the pig producers and the bacon curers. These contracts were based in the first instance on a standard price for pigs which varied with the market price of a standard food ration (largely imported) for the pigs. The contract was not related in any way to the price of bacon; so that when bacon prices did not rise, (as anticipated under the quota import restrictions), the curers suffered heavy losses. For this they were indemnified by a loan guaranteed by the Government and repaid by a subsequent levy on producers. Subsequent contracts made allowance for the price of bacon. These, however, broke down through the inability of the curers to get the number of pigs contracted for, and the Pigs Board were forced to allow them to buy in the open market. The whole scheme, finally, was found to be unworkable and in 1938 the Government had to begin all over again.

The pig industry is now governed by the Bacon Industry Act, 1938. Under that Act the price to be received by the pig producer from the curers is based on a standard figure varying with the price of feeding-stuffs and staggered slightly over 12 months in an endeavour to counteract market fluctuations. Curers, however, are guaranteed by the Government against any loss they may suffer, when the price of bacon falls below 94/9d. per cwt. The import quotas were also to be relaxed until the price did fall below that figure. It is estimated that the subsidy will amount to £1 million a year.

Thus stability of prices would, it was hoped, be ensured to both producers and curers. But whether the curers can get sufficient pigs at the contract prices depends upon the profitableness of bacon-pig production and on the state of the pork market. This latter consideration is of importance, for the pork market is an uncontrolled open market. Now, a pig can be turned into either of two alternative products; pork, accounting for two-thirds of the total output, and cured meat (bacon and ham) accounting for the remainder. The pig is generally killed for pork at the age of 5 months and for bacon at 8 or 9 months. Thus, at a given moment pigs can be turned either to the pork market or reserved for the bacon · market later, according to the anticipation of producers as to future prices. The earlier scheme broke down partly because when the curing factories were short of pigs they went into the pork market and offered prices above the contract price for pigs which might be used for bacon and ham. Further reasons for the breakdown of the first scheme were the continuance of the pig cycle which legislation modified but did not obliterate, and the personnel of the Pigs Board which had to start work without time to train a technical staff.

Bacon Development Board and Future Policy

The Bacon Development Board, as its name implies, is concerned solely with bacon (to the exclusion of pork).

The 1938 Act gave it increased powers to improve the efficiency of both sides of the bacon industry and in particular for rationalising the bacon factories of the country. The Pigs and Bacon Boards will in practice act in an advisory and administrative capacity to carry out the policy laid down by the Development Board.

The Development Board has, during its four years of existence, laid the foundations of schemes of research and experiments in the production of pigs and bacon; and if provided with sufficient funds for these purposes, great benefits to the industry must accrue. For if there is one lesson which stands out from this story of attempted re-organization it is that so long as our bacon is of such inferior general average quality (always excepting the small output of the best Wiltshire bacon) it must prove exceedingly difficult to compete successfully with the Danes. Even if this results partly from the housewife's prejudice against what she considers an inferior article, it will take a long time and a very steady supply of consistently good quality British bacon to eradicate that prejudice. There has been a noticeable improvement in the last four years due to the grading systems introduced by the Pigs Board, and the encouragement given to better quality production, but there is still much to be done.

Our ordinary methods of improving agricultural efficiency do not adequately cover pig production. The Ministry of Agriculture has Commissioners or special departments for dairying, poultry and fruit, but not for pig husbandry.

Even if substantial progress were to be made in breeding, in feeding technique, in housing and other matters, and even assuming the most satisfactory and efficient methods of curing and marketing, it is very doubtful whether there would be room for any large expansion of this industry in Britain unless accompanied by very vigorous restriction of Danish imports, at the expense of the consumer. The Danes have the advantage of being able to utilize in pig production a by-product (skimmed milk) of their butter industry, which gives them an overwhelming advantage in

the cost of feeding. Skim milk contains all the constituents of whole milk except the butter fat. Thus every
gallon of skimmed milk contains about 1 lb. of invaluable
minerals, proteins and sugar which the British pig feeder must
buy in meals from abroad at much higher cost. And since
the role of the British dairy industry will be to produce,
in the main, liquid milk and not butter, our farmers cannot
hope to enjoy this natural advantage. Drastic import
restrictions cannot be justified on economic grounds. Our
trade with Denmark is of a highly reciprocal character,
based on the advantages of specialization which natural
conditions have conferred on each country. To diminish
this interchange substantially would inevitably injure
certain of our exporting industries and at the same time
have an unfortunate influence on our good relations with
Denmark and other friendly neutral European countries
and perhaps throw them into the arms of a possible enemy.

The Government has produced a long-term policy which
provides the pig industry with a subsidy of £1 million per
annum and which appears skilfully devised to give some
benefit to producers and curers. Yet it is difficult to
believe that the new scheme will be successful. As we
have pointed out, it still leaves the market for pork pigs
uncontrolled, an omission which may well prove fatal,
especially since the free market will make for the continuance of the pig cycle, with all the fluctuations and dis-
locations which that entails. In any case we cannot believe
that a general subsidy of this kind is a wise expenditure
of public money. From the point of view of agriculture
as a whole, the money could certainly be spent to better
advantage; while from the point of view of the pig industry,
the immediate needs are more for improvement in the
quality and reliability of the product.

It should not be made the central aim of policy for
the pig industry to foster an artificial expansion of
bacon which could only be achieved by drastic restriction of imports or larger subsidies. Nor do we favour
control of the pork industry. Instead the Government

should encourage technical progress in quality and efficiency, so that this branch of farming may establish itself on a firmer basis and may become better equipped to take its natural share of the market. Pig production should, as in the past, remain a by-product of farming. As a by-product Britain can produce profitably about three to four million pigs per year. More than that must be paid for as a luxury by the consumer or taxpayer directly or indirectly. It should not be encouraged to become a major industry, especially as it is almost solely dependent on imported feeding-stuffs.

CHAPTER XIV

POULTRY

THE fourth branch of live-stock—poultry—has two separate branches, eggs and table birds (which latter suffers incidentally from a by-product of the first, i.e., an enormous quantity of aged hens which depresses the market). Before 1914 fowl flocks on general farms were of a dual purpose character. Since the war the production of table fowls has become subsidiary to eggs.

Poultry farming has expanded on a scale unrivalled by any other branch of farming in post-war years. There are now about half a million poultry-keepers in Great Britain. After allowing for those not in the business primarily for commercial profit the significant fact emerges that more people are concerned with egg-production than in any other branch of agriculture.

Figures showing the rapid expansion are remarkable. The poultry population in England, Wales and Scotland rose from 47 millions in 1924 to 90 million in 1934, the percentage increase being highest in England, i.e., 110 per cent. Since 1934 there has been a slight decline.

Why was there this phenomenal expansion? The chief reason was that though prices of eggs and poultry fell the prices of the feeding-stuffs, the chief item in cost of production, fell still more steeply. Another reason was the relative unprofitableness of other sides of farming. In the hard-hit arable counties farmers found in poultry a useful subsidiary income. A third reason was the ease with which one can build up a poultry business. The capital for a backyard flock is negligible; poultry houses can be built by hand; stock can be enlarged out of home produced eggs; in fact the only outgoings are for poultry foods paid for out of receipts from the sale of eggs. Turn-over is so rapid that a man with energy and ability, even starting with no capital might build up a flock of 1,000 birds within two years. Wherever there is ready access to retail markets, where smallholdings are available and where unemployment is fairly severe, new entrants readily find their way into the industry. An example of this is Lancashire, now the dominant poultry county of England.

Producers may be roughtly classified as, the back-garden producer, accounting for nearly half of the total output of eggs and poultry meat; the barn-door flock kept by the farmer's wife or daughter who does not sell eggs regularly; farms devoted entirely to poultry and farms where poultry management is only one side of mixed farming. Of these last two the mixed farmer is the more important. His share in the total egg output is probably some two and a half times that of the specialist poultry keeper.

The commercial egg producer does not, as a rule, breed his stock. That is the business of specialised breeding farms which sell hatching eggs, day-old chicks, and pullets.

Producers' Problems

Laying record and freedom from disease are the two most important factors in the pedigree behind hatching eggs and young chicks. Laying record can be tested at trials, while freedom from disease is encouraged by the Ministry of Agriculture Accredited Breeders Scheme.

There are "A" breeders whose entire flocks must pass the agglutination test (resistance to bacillary white diarrhoea and carrying fowl typhoid) and "B" breeders who have only their breeding pen so tested. The working of this scheme has not proved satisfactory and the majority of specialist breeders remain outside it.

Whether breeders concentrate too much on laying records and not enough on resistance to disease, or whether incubation is unskilfully managed, it is in hatching that the heavy losses begin which run all through the poultry industry. Inexperience and inefficiency among breeders may account for part of the hatching losses but since dead germs, dead in shell and weak chicks account for most of it the root cause is lack of stamina in the parent stock.

During rearing, especially in the brooder, further losses are incurred. One comprehensive survey showed that 11·3 per cent of chicks transferred from incubators were lost in the brooder stage. A further 5 per cent were lost before the birds began to lay, i.e. before they were 6 months old. Without taking account of cockerels destroyed for commercial reasons, only half the original hatching eggs become adult birds.

Once the sex of the birds is determined the table-poultry and egg-producing industries part company. In rearing birds for poultry meat it takes between 14 and 20 weeks for birds after emerging from the brooder to reach a weight of 4 lbs. Feeding the birds up for this purpose is costly compared with other meats, because they consume large quantities of food for the flesh they put on. This limits the possibilities of expanding the market. The portion of the market which can be provided by specialist table-poultry producers is also limited because throw-outs from the egg-laying flocks provide about two-thirds of the total supply. The remaining third is supplied partly by egg producers as a side line and only to a very small extent by specialists. It requires greater skill and experience to rear and fatten table-poultry successfully than to produce eggs. The bulk of chicken meat consists of culls and old hens fattened up for which any price above scrap value is a gain, and it is their output which determines the price of all but the finest table-birds.

We must now return to the pullets which at the age of 6 months are transferred to the laying-flock for the egg-producing side of the industry. Here commercial success depends chiefly on good stock and management including housing, feeding, level production and low rate of depreciation.

Poultry housing has remarkably improved in ventilation, insulation from cold, and so forth. The dark and dirty back-yard shed is being replaced by movable arks. The most striking innovation of all is the battery system by which birds are reared in small pens with wire floors, through which droppings fall.

A further development has been the proper balancing of food rations. The tendency to-day is towards greater use of mashes in place of wheat and maize. The price of the feeding-stuff representing 60 per cent of the cost of egg production is most important. Ability to buy foods 10 per cent cheaper through a Co-operative Society or by purchasing in bulk instead of on credit from a dealer may make a difference of 6d. in profit per bird.

There is room for improvement by reducing the seasonality of output. In the peak month (April) the output is two and a half times the output of the lowest month (November). These variations in output lead not only to price fluctuations but slow down consumers' demands. After eggs have been dear for a period it takes weeks of lower prices to induce the public to begin eating them again. Hatching might be spread out more evenly in the year. By warming and electrically lighting the poultry house in winter more regular yields could be obtained and these are also generally accompanied by higher yields. A high-yielding hen usually keeps on laying more regularly all the year round.

Annual yields have risen steadily from 72 per hen in 1908 to 100 in 1924, 120 in 1930/31 and probably a higher figure since, with instances at egg-laying trials of hens laying up to 300 eggs a year. The search for high yields may, however, go too far and prejudice the birds' constitution. Probably a flock average of well under 200 eggs a year is ample.

A problem continually before the poultry farmer is to minimize the rate of depreciation of his stock. Birds which go off laying must be ruthlessly weeded out—some after a month or two; a large number after the first laying season, the best only being kept for a second season.

Probably about 50 per cent of the laying flocks are withdrawn every year. That gives a total life to the bird of two years or a laying life of 1½ years. On top of this, between 10 and 20 per cent of the birds die of disease. The Poultry Technical Committee in 1938 took a grave view of this aspect. They found poultry stocks riddled with debility and disease all over the country. They quote an authoritative estimate that the losses among adult birds alone cost the industry £4 millions per annum (equal to one-fifth of the gross output of eggs). This is an overwhelming handicap and one which no individual producer can entirely overcome, even though buying reliable stock and wise management reduce it. As a result, receipts of poultry farmers show immense fluctuations. One of the obvious needs of the industry is to reduce disease.

Marketing

The disposal of eggs and table poultry varies according to local circumstances. In Lancashire where the poultry farms are in close contact with a dense consuming population, a large part of the output is producer retailed. The remainder is bought by higglers at the farms or weekly markets. In some rural areas the weekly market is more important. In wholly rural and remote districts where producers are scattered and other market facilities are bad, a system of trading has arisen through packing stations owned mostly by private firms but in some cases by associations of producers.

The grading of eggs is an important element in the price and certain size gradings by weights have been established under the "Agricultural Produce (Grading and Marking) Acts". Grading according to quality seems as yet unattainable.

As the principal element in quality is freshness the circuitousness of egg marketing presents a serious problem. Cases of eggs have been marketed and found to take up to three weeks to reach the consumer, whilst Danish eggs take only four or five days although they come across the sea. The Reorganization Commission (1935) recommended a marketing board with a chain of 200 packing stations, each with a radius of ten miles. The scheme was rejected by the producers because of its compulsory character. However, some control is about to be instituted by the establishment of a Poultry Commission, intended primarily to devise means for combating disease, the industry also has an Advisory Committee set up to make recommendations for improving marketing arrangements.

Any Commission which attempts to supervise egg marketing will sooner or later be involved in price-fixing. Now the arbitrary fixing of egg prices will prove a more delicate task than the fixing of milk prices, since the Spring glut of eggs cannot be dumped on to a separate manufacturing market, as in the case of milk, but must be sold off at reduced prices. The seasonal variation in egg prices is great. This may be remedied by improvements in storage technique: cold storage of eggs having become feasible; and still more recently gas storage has been developed, keeping the eggs, it is claimed, in as good condition as new-laid eggs. Storage would be too expensive for any but the largest producers and will more probably be developed by packing stations.

Imports

After fluctuations, our imports in 1936 were about 2,400 million eggs (about 55 eggs per head of the population). Our imports have, since 1912, constituted a progressively smaller proportion of our total supplies. In 1912 imports of eggs in shells were 63 per cent of our supplies, in 1924 48 per cent and in 1935–6 36 per cent. Imports are now controlled by agreements with foreign countries and by tariffs.

Under these, imports are diminished during our own peak output (April and May) and are larger in October when supplies are relatively short at home.

Imported eggs compete effectively in price and quality with the British. These sources of supplies are important for the lower income groups as eggs constitute a food rich in proteins, vitamins and mineral salts.

Future Prospects

From the point of view of National nutrition, there ought undoubtedly to be a large increase in egg consumption even though this rose from 104 per head in 1909–13 to 150 in 1934–35 and 159 in 1938; and though compared with other countries with lower standards of living, we eat more eggs (only Canada, the United States, and Belgium are ahead of us) our relatively high consumption is due to our breakfast menu added to the use of eggs in cakes, puddings, sauces, etc., at other meals.

Large sections, especially the lower income groups, must consume well under 50 per head per annum. Consumption is restricted principally by the price of eggs and particularly by the regular rise in price in the autumn and winter, from which the demand recovers only sluggishly when prices fall in the Spring. The principal objectives in the egg industry, therefore, should be to reduce costs of production and seasonality of output.

The factor in costs most susceptible to reduction is depreciation. The industry needs concerted efforts at better breeding to improve the quality of the laying stock, and a more vigorous attack on diseases.

The working of the Accredited Breeders Scheme has not proved satisfactory. This Scheme divides breeders into two classes: "A" breeders whose entire flock have passed certain blood tests, and "B" breeders who have only their breeding pen so tested. The inspectorate is inadequate and there are many opportunities for evasion. The "B" Scheme has few merits and should be abolished, because recent research suggests that all stock on a farm needs testing if any of it is to be considered safe. The remedy appears to be thorough inspection and legislation to regulate the sale of hatching eggs and young stock from non-inspected flocks.

The Poultry Technical Committee have recommended the compulsory registration of distributors of stock, hatching-eggs and day-old chicks; the institution of a grading scheme on voluntary lines for breeding farms, with State assistance by way of premiums and free veterinary services; the establishment of progeny testing stations for the production of foundation breeding stock; the reorganization of conditions governing auction sales and disposals; the examination of the position in regard to imports of breeding stock and hatching-eggs; and increased provision for research and education in poultry problems. They further recommended the establishment of a Poultry (Stock Improvement) Commission for Great Britain. Such a Commission has just been set up (1939). It is empowered to implement most of the proposals made by the Poultry Technical Committee. Every distributor of poultry stock will have to register and observe the Commission's regulations. Wide powers are given to the Commission to put an end to unsatisfactory breeding arrangements and to replacements.

On the marketing side, there is probably less room for improvement than in the case of many agricultural products. The costs of egg distribution probably only add to the producer's price something between 25 and 50 per cent according to the district and time of year, as compared with from 75 to 100 per cent in the case of meat and milk. A notable development of recent years has been the country packing stations which, partly by cutting out certain intermediaries, and partly by grading, have been able to offer the farmer better prices than the dealer. The packing-station method is likely to grow, to the benefit of the industry. We do not consider that a national marketing scheme is desirable at present, though it may be more practicable later, if packing stations become more widespread. The new Commission is to put a scheme of grading into operation. Retailers will be required to sell graded produce and wholesalers, who will have to be registered, will be required to undertake grading. The Government also proposes to offer loans for the establishment of producers' co-operative packing stations.

Meanwhile it is important not to restrict unduly our supplies of eggs from abroad. The bulk of these, from Denmark, Holland and Empire countries, are high-quality eggs marketed at a price which brings them within the reach of sections of the community which otherwise would consume very few. Moreover, these supplies are far less seasonal in character than our own.

At the same time, the British poultry industry is in a more exposed position than other branches of agriculture. Not only do poultry keepers have to face the competition of egg imports, but they are peculiarly dependent on the prices of imported feeding-stuffs, which constitute the major element in their costs of production; egg production like pig production is primarily a processing industry. Under these circumstances poultry producers have a claim to some measure of assistance. But in the case of eggs it would be inappropriate to establish a price-insurance scheme such as has been advocated for other products. The price of British eggs depends quite as much on the price of feeding-stuffs as on the price of imported eggs; and to tie a guaranteed price to changes in the latter, while ignoring the former, might give rise to serious anomalies. We accordingly favour instead the retention of the present import duty, which, being a specific duty, has the advantage of reducing the seasonality of imported supplies.

CHAPTER XV

MILK PRODUCTION

MILK is unquestionably the most important product of British agriculture, both to the farmer and consumer. It is most truly the corner-stone of our agriculture; in value it accounts for over one-quarter of the output; it is twice as important as any other single commodity; it is produced by a multitude of farmers, large and small, in every part of the land; it brings them a dependable cash income all through the year; and in liquid form, it enjoys natural protection from foreign competition.

For the nation milk is a vital food—essential for healthy diet. To attain an optimum standard of nutrition national consumption might be doubled. In recent years there has been a slight increase due to extensive advertising and propaganda, yet, our average consumption of milk per head of the population is very much less than that of most European countries and of America.

There are two prerequisites to any expansion of the liquid milk market. Milk must be safe and it must be reasonably cheap.

Public fears of milk as a source of infection are widespread, and whilst to some extent these fears are exaggerated, it is true that our milk supplies still leave much to be desired.

The price of milk is also a hindrance to increased consumption. But to keep down the price and at the same time improve quality and maintain and, perhaps, enlarge production, is no easy matter. No economies would materially reduce the retail price unless effective in both the producing and distributing sections of the industry.

Grass and Arable Dairying

Milk comes to us from a variety of producers, working under all sorts of conditions. There are small-holders with two or three cows, and family farmers with a fair-sized dairy herd. A few undertake milk production on a big scale. Some combine it with store-cattle raising, others with mixed arable farming. This variety of types of dairying accounts for the astonishing variations in the cost of milk production—variations which are probably larger than for almost any other product.

Nevertheless there are two main methods of dairy farming. The first combines milk production with arable farming and is found mostly in the drier Eastern counties. The cows' food, by far the most important factor in production costs, consists partly of by-products of the field crops, but largely of food bought in the form of concentrates. As the latter is expensive, this intensive system depends for success on nearness to the liquid milk market or on a higher price which is often associated with winter milk.

The second system is carried on in the grasslands of the moister Northern and Western counties. Costs are low. The cows are fed more on grass than on concentrates, and give more milk when the pastures are at their best in May and June, so that there are big seasonal fluctuations in this type of production. Transport costs for many years kept these producers out of the liquid market, the milk being converted into cheese or butter, or used for calves.

In the future we may see a narrowing of the differences between these two methods. On the one hand more arable land, even in the Eastern counties, may go down to temporary grass; on the other hand more of the permanent pastures may come under the plough and be converted into temporary pastures, so that the Western type of dairying will spread Eastwards. The new technique of grassland management (Ch. IV) should also reduce the fluctuation between summer flush and winter shortage. As arable farming tends to diminish it is essential that grassland dairy farmers should make better use of their grass, for economical grass production will be the basis of economical milk production. Improvement in grassland management should certainly lead to a reduction in the farm cost of milk.

Cost of Feeding Cows

Much of the success of dairy farming depends on the efficient and economical provision of feeding-stuffs. Between 1934 and 1937 a careful investigation into the cost of milk production was conducted by the Agricultural Economics Research Institute, Oxford, assisted by the Advisory Economists at eleven colleges and universities (covering England and Wales). Data from about 600 herds situated in all the chief dairying districts covered a wide variety of methods of production. The Reports which, before being published, were approved by a conference of leading Agricultural Economists, show that wide variation in costs exist between farm and farm, ranging from 5d. to 1s. 9d. per gallon. The figures indicate that of the total costs of production, food accounts for 58 per cent of the cost, labour for 22 per cent, other items for 12 per cent and herd replacement for 8 per cent.

Food then is the chief item and labour the next, between them accounting for 80 per cent. It is obvious that faulty management, inexperience, carelessness in the purchase of feeding-stuffs, in the rations arranged or in the quantity given to individual cows, will easily increase costs considerably and unnecessarily. Similarly inability to organize labour to the best advantage can put up costs. In fact the ability of individual farmers, whether natural ability or acquired from close study of the experience of others, is the deciding factor in efficiency, in profit and in reducing production costs.

Labour costs in Milk Production

The second most important element in costs is labour.

One of the most interesting experiments in the economic use of labour and equipment is the system of open-air dairying originated by Mr. Hosier. The cows live in the fields day and night, winter and summer, and the milking is done in light, movable sheds on wheels. This dispenses entirely with the old and often expensive cow houses and a great deal of unnecessary labour in carting food-stuffs and manure.

Other advantages of this system, coupled with machine milking, are the small capital equipment compared with the orthodox cow-shed system, the saving in fencing and the improvement in the quality of the pastures under the combined treading and manuring round the sheds. By moving these sheds at intervals over the field, the whole pasture is improved and a reserve of fertility derived from the concentrates eaten by the cows is built up, which can be turned to advantage periodically by arable cultivation.

Those who have practised this system have found it highly profitable. It has proved that cows can be kept in the open air all the year round (even in Caithness, York-shire and on the bleak downs of Wiltshire), and that their health seems better than that of cows kept indoors. It is a system specially suited to present-day conditions in which the most labour-saving methods of production stand the greatest chance of success. However it requires light soil and is especially suited to large farms, so that the main stumbling blocks to its more general use are the small average size of farms and clay soil.

Length of Life of the Cow

Another factor affecting the milk problem is the length of life of the cow. This has received too little attention from farmers and agricultural economists. The length of active, *healthy* herd life of the British milk cow is far too short. From investigations made by dairy research institutes, milk recording societies, and calculations based on our annual agricultural returns, the average herd life (i.e. the period during which she is yielding milk) of the English cow is slightly shorter than that of the Scottish cow and probably three years shorter than the Irish cow.

With a milking life of only four years, the ability of a herd to maintain itself is extremely doubtful. English dairy farmers are not disposed to give much attention to the rearing of calves. They concentrate on milk and sell off the calves for veal soon after birth. As a result, the main herd has been maintained by imports of cows and heifers. From Ireland 40,000–80,000 milch cows and springers are brought every year; that is about 10 per cent of the total entrants into the English dairy herd. Ireland can afford to spare so many of her heifers because with a herd life of seven to eight years she has a surplus for export.

Yields

What are the causes of this early mortality among cattle in England ? There is no very conclusive answer but it seems probable that the demand for high yielding cows and the intensive system of milk production practised in this country are contributory factors owing to the strain imposed on the cow's constitution. Another disadvantage of this practice is that maximum yield does not necessarily mean maximum profit as, after a certain output has been reached, a cow's yield will not increase proportionately to the extra food given to her.

The ideal which has been laid before farmers and encouraged by agricultural shows, feeding-stuffs manufacturers, and rearing and breeding societies,—that of attaining the maximum yield per cow—is a false one, and it is therefore not surprising to find quite frequently the unorthodox farmer with "poor" stock, low yields, but still lower costs, making better profits than the "superior" farmer with a high class of stock and high yields. This is the experience of Wye Agricultural College, in their investigations in Kent.

As long as the average yield throughout the country was very low, the ideal of a high milk yield provided a good rough guide to the improvement of cattle. But there are signs that this ideal has served its turn and may now become an actual handicap to improvement. It is likely that the future of the British dairy industry lies in the direction of low costs and long lives rather than in high yields and fancy breeds.

Disease

The wastage of dairy cows through disease (tuberculosis, abortion, sterility, Johne's disease, mastitis, foot and mouth disease) presents a very grave problem in the industry. This was revealed in striking fashion by special investigations made in Scotland (1929), Cambridge (1928–30), Reading (1929), and six Southern counties (1930), each investigation covering from 9,000 to 13,000 cows. The result showed that about 50 per cent of all the cows were disposed of through some form of disease. Not more than 5 per cent died of old age.

Two of the most serious diseases are tuberculosis and contagious abortion. The Public Health Committee of the L.C.C. reported in 1933 that 83 per cent of the milk arriving in London in glass tanks contained tubercle bacilli. The Economic Advisory Council's Committee on Cattle Diseases estimated that 40 per cent of our cows would react to the tuberculin test. There are about 5,000 cases each year of people suffering from bovine tuberculosis and about 2,000 to 3,000 deaths.[1] This aspect of the question is of the greatest immediate importance both to public health and as inflicting a loss to farmers. Contagious abortion though less in the public eye is equally important, whilst "mastitis" (a generic term given to udder affections) may cause even greater losses to farmers.

The reasons for the diseased condition of the British dairy

[1] Journal of the Ministry of Agriculture. 1932.

herd are not altogether clear. Besides the intensive system of production, the unusual extent to which animals are moved about is another factor. Only a very small proportion of the total cow population is in "closed" herds. The risk of spreading disease is therefore great, especially as it is the unsatisfactory, but not too *visibly* unsatisfactory animals, which tend to be sold from one herd to another. Further, even healthy beasts, when in transit, are liable to infection in vans, trucks and market places.

Government measures for cleaning up the dairy herd have up to the present been inadequate. Localization of the veterinary service has hampered uniform standards. The policy of slaughtering (with compensation) may have lessened the sale of highly infected animals but it has done little to eradicate disease.

Graded Milk

Probably the only effective method of eradicating disease is the segregation of disease-free herds. Producers have done this to some extent on a voluntary basis. We have the "tuberculin tested" herds from which came milk of the old designations "Certified" and "Grade A, T.T." The number of such herds has hitherto been small.

In 1935 the Government instituted a scheme for "attested herds", under which tuberculin testing was carried out free, and milk from "attested herds" was given a bonus of 1d. per gallon. By the end of 1937, there were 1,453 "attested herds", with some 90,000 cows, i.e. less than 3 per cent. of all the cows in the country.

Another scheme for cleaner, as opposed to safer, milk has been the "Accredited Producers" Scheme of the Milk Marketing Board with a bonus of 1d. per gallon raised from a levy on all milk sold. This also met with a limited success covering about 10 per cent of the producers. Both schemes have only been in operation a short time.

In the autumn of 1938 the Government introduced a Bill which among other provisions increased the premiums for milk produced under more hygienic conditions. This Bill aroused some agitation and was withdrawn as a result of opposition from interests other than those of the consumer.

In July 1939 the Government introduced a revised but considerably emaciated version of the Milk Bill withdrawn in February. It was another temporary measure, continuing existing assistance for encouraging tubercle free herds, for cheap milk schemes and for guaranteeing a remunerative price for milk used in manufacturing butter and cheese. This Act [the Milk Industry (No. 2) Act] shirked three major problems faced by the old Bill which was dropped, viz. (i) Setting up a Milk Commission to have the final say in price fixing instead of leaving this to the (Producers') Milk Board. The Act sets up a Consumers' Committee but as it is only a consultative body it cannot have adequate power. (ii) The rationalisation of distribution. (iii) The provision of powers for making pasteurization compulsory on the request of a Local Authority. The consumer, therefore, is still without adequate provision of safer and cheaper liquid milk.

It may be that a mere money bonus will not prove strong enough to effect that rapid improvement in the quality of the supply of raw milk which the public has been led to expect; and that more direct attention will have to be given by the Government to cleaning up our herds. Until this is done and as long as the risk of "re-infection" remains so high, the cost to the farmer of producing milk of satisfactory quality will remain high. The need of removing disease of all sorts from our dairy cattle cannot be too strongly emphasised since it is a main reason for the shortness of the length of life of the average cow.

The cost, and time required for eradicating disease provide a strong argument for the adoption of officially supervised pasteurization for all milk whose hygienic quality cannot be guaranteed. We deal with pasteurization elsewhere.

G

Lines of Future Policy

Our producers, whether working on an arable or grassland system, cannot escape the criticism that their production costs are too high by comparison with the dairy farmers of Holland and Denmark. As already pointed out, the recent authoritative investigations indicate that 58 per cent of the cost of milk production represents the cost of food and 22 per cent the cost of labour.[1] They also show (as did earlier reports) enormous variations in the cost of production between farm and farm. These facts taken together seem to point to the need for improved technique, organization and management on many farms, as well as to the probability that some dairy farms are submarginal owing to conditions beyond the farmer's control.

Fortunately it is here that the State can lend enormous help by seeing that advice and example are made available, as well as by continued research. The State can assist the industry further by more vigorously investigating and eradicating disease, by subsidizing better bulls and providing more veterinary assistance, so helping to lengthen the average milk yielding life of the cow, by stimulating the production of better quality milk, and by tightening up preventive legislation which enforces certain minimum standards of hygiene and cleanliness.

[1] (Cutforth) Milk Reorganisation Commission; (Luke) Advisory Committee on Nutrition of the Ministry of Health; (Gowland Hopkins) Committee on Cattle Diseases of the Economic Advisory Council; Ministry of Health and Department of Health for Scotland report " The Nutritive Value of Milk " 1936. Board of Education " Circular 1437 ", 193 Cd. British Medical Association.

CHAPTER XVI

MILK MARKETING

THE history of the milk market over the last fifty years has been one of change—from local to ever widening markets; from small to large distributive units; from rough and ready transport and delivery to more and more refined methods leading to the present day bottling, pasteurization, etc; from day to day bargaining to long term contracts; from individual and collective bargaining methods to a system of complete National control through bodies such as the Milk Marketing Boards.

As is known, though often forgotten when discussing policy, milk can be sold either as a finished article of consumption or used as the raw material of conversion into manufactured products, e.g. butter, cheese, dried milk. Before the War, the difference in price for milk sent to the liquid market and milk used for butter, etc., did not vary so greatly and owing to the cost of transport dairy farmers situated far from London actually obtained relatively more for manufacturing milk than for liquid milk. During the War control aimed at encouraging the sale of liquid milk and discouraging the consumption of butter.

In the early attempts at collective bargaining between the National Farmers' Union and the National Federation of Dairymen's Associations and subsequently through a permanent Joint Milk Council, the contracts made were usually based on the assumed existence of two markets and two prices for milk, a liquid high priced and a manufacturing low priced market; each farmer being paid a higher liquid price for his average winter production and a lower manufacturing price for any excess (ordinarily a summer excess). This was called the "basic surplus" principle.

The manufacturing price for 1922 to 1929 was based on the average world price of cheese, i.e. on the price of milk required to produce a given quantity of cheese. From 1929–30 onward the system disintegrated, as the cost of milk for manufacturing dropped owing to decrease in the world price of cheese and butter; for instance, the manufacturing price which in 1923 had been $\frac{1}{2}d.$ more than the liquid price in 1933 was $4\cdot7d.$ less. When prices collapsed in the 1930–31 slump, the old contract systems broke down and the price of liquid milk threatened to fall heavily. The advent of road transport enabled those working for the manufacturing milk market to turn their milk into the liquid market to fetch what it could, which was generally much below the contract price for liquid milk. It was then that the State stepped in and gave producers powers to establish the Milk Marketing Boards for England and Scotland under the Agricultural Marketing Acts of 1931 and 1933. If there had been no legislation collective bargaining might have disappeared and there would have been disorganization and widespread distress for dairy farmers. In the long run the consumer might have had cheaper milk but such speculation is academic.

The Milk Marketing Board for England and Wales consists of 17 members of whom 15 are elected by dairy farmers and 2 are co-opted. With minor exceptions, all producers who wish to sell milk must be registered and no one, except these registered producers, is permitted to sell milk. So to-day the sale of milk is regulated by a contract between the producer and the distributor,[1] drawn up by the Board each year after consultation with the Central Milk Distributors' Committee.

About 1,080 million gallons of milk were sold through the Board in 1938–9 representing a wholesale revenue of £52,613,790. The Milk Board is thus one of the greatest financial concerns in the country.

The wholesale price for each month is specified in the contract, being higher in winter months: the price for

[1] Special provision is made in the Scheme for producer retailers.

milk sold for making milk products is lower than for liquid milk: no milk can be sold at prices below those specified: all payments between farmers and distributors are made through the Board by means of "pools". Factories for milk products also make their payments into these pools.

Producers receive payment on the same basis, i.e., the ratio of each farmer's milk paid for at liquid and manufacturing prices respectively is the same as the ratio of the total supply of milk sold to the liquid and manufacturing markets. This has a very considerable effect on the farmer's receipts. When the Milk Scheme started in 1933 roughly 75 per cent of the milk went to the liquid and 25 per cent to the manufacturing market. A farmer accordingly received liquid price for about 75 and manufacturing price for 25 out of every 100 gallons, regardless of the actual use made or the destination of his own milk. This method of payment still occurs, but by 1938 the ratios had altered from 75 and 25 to about 70 and 30. Assuming a constant wholesale price of 14d. per gallon for liquid and of 6d. for manufacturing milk, in 1933 a farmer would have received £5 for 100 gallons (i.e. 75 x 14 + 25 x 6, a total of 1200d. or an average of 12d. per gallon), whereas in 1938 he would have received £4 16s. 8d. for 100 gallons (i.e. 70 x 14 x 30 x 6, a total of 1160d. or an average of 11s. 6d. per gallon).[1]

If one had to provide for no fluctuations in supply or demand and no contingencies, if that is to say, the farmer received 14d., which is what the consumer pays, for the whole of his 100 gallons he would get £5 16s. 8d.

These figures serve to prove two things, firstly how unremunerative is the turning of milk into dairy products and therefore how unwise it is to aim at building up a butter and cheese industry here: and secondly how short-

[1] These approximate prices and figures are sufficiently close to illustrate the operation of the scheme on a farmer's revenue. To prevent confusion the illustration omits any reference to minor details such as charges for administration, transport, bonuses, premiums, etc.

sighted it is for farmers to oppose pasteurization. Many members of the medical profession and Medical Officers of Health are unwilling to join a Drink More Milk Campaign or to urge parents to give their children more milk because they know full well the ravages of bovine tuberculosis and that periodically the community suffers from such other diseases as are at times milk borne such as typhoid, scarlet fever, diphtheria, etc. Risk of infection can be avoided by pasteurization without any serious damage to the nutritive properties of milk as has been authoritatively confirmed by all recent reports and studies.

If milk were rendered safer by pasteurization, farmers would sell more gallons at a high liquid price and fewer at a low manufacturing price. Raising the price of butter and cheese by restricting imports, which some farmers ask for, would not benefit them so much as convincing the public that they can drink milk without risk. In attested herds special precautions are taken to protect calves from bovine tuberculosis. Regulations drafted by the Ministry of Agriculture and accepted by Parliament and dairy farmers insist that in order to safeguard the health of these calves they shall be given no milk unless it comes from a guaranteed tubercle free herd or has been pasteurized. Mothers are surely entitled to demand that their children shall be afforded equal protection!

The increase in the proportion of milk sold to the liquid and manufacturing markets is largely due to the fact that when the liquid market was glutted the Government and Milk Board[1] subsidized (i.e., reduced the loss on) manufacturing milk. In ordinary business an over-supply is followed by a reduction in price till supply and demand are equated. A gradual reduction in price by the Board would have removed the more inefficient producers and achieved the same result as competition, but without any fear of dislocation by a sudden ruinous drop in price. The disparity between the prices of liquid and manufactured milk tends to become greater as the proportion of the

[1] By what amounts to a concealed levy on milk drinkers.

surplus for manufacturing increases. This is costly to the consumer and disadvantageous to the producer.

Past experience shows that a certain surplus is necessary in winter when output drops as a reserve for contingencies and market fluctuations. The Reorganization Commission advocated limiting the surplus over the requirements of the liquid market to 20 per cent of normal requirements over the year. They further suggested that if the milk used for cream were regarded as part of the available reserve, a lower percentage of about 10 per cent would be required. This winter surplus would suffice to meet contingencies and fluctuations.

The Food Council also recommended limiting the application of the pool price to the quantity of milk necessary for the liquid market plus a reserve margin. They did not consider it in the national interest to subsidize or encourage by import restriction butter and cheese making.

The price of milk is not only affected by the relative proportions sold for liquid consumption and for conversion into milk products; it is also controlled by another device.

The Board divided England and Wales into 11 regions. The costs of milk production vary considerably in different parts of England, being affected by rainfall and other considerations. The total receipts for the sale of milk for each region, whatever use the milk is put to, and whatever price the buyer pays for it, together with government subsidies (and contributions from producer retailers) are paid into a *regional* pool for that district. In order that farmers in regions which have a very large proportion of the low priced manufacturing milk should not receive much less than farmers in regions with higher proportions of liquid sales, a special levy of 1d. to 1½d. per gallon on all *liquid* sales is imposed and paid into an "interregional compensation fund". This is a device for transferring part of the receipts of farmers producing for the liquid market to farmers producing for the manufacturing market, and is part of the machinery for keeping the latter off the liquid market which would thereby bring down the price of liquid milk. In fact the scheme involves a payment by Eastern farmers to the Westerners for not spoiling prices in their liquid market and in practice they pay about £1 million.

It is easy to criticize this procedure from the consumers' point of view. If price-fixing powers had been vested in a Joint Milk Council, as recommended by the Grigg Commission, events might have been otherwise. But, in practice, the Milk Board, as set up, was a farmers' Board elected by dairy farmers and responsible to farmers only. Consequently the Board attempted to make the best bargain it could for farmers as a whole.

When Parliament passed the Marketing Act a clause was included whereby a Consumers' Council was to be set up—but (as was noted by the Cutforth Reorganization Commission) its powers are so restricted that it is ineffective as an instrument for looking after the public interest. The Food Council—a body also created to safeguard the public by publicity though it again has no effective power—has repeatedly drawn attention to the injustices now suffered by the public and has, like the Cutforth Commission, recommended that price fixing and policy should no longer be entrusted to the present Milk Board, which is in effect a Producers' Monopoly.

The Milk Marketing Board in Scotland does not differ in any essential principle from the English Board in its methods of fixing prices.

In Northern Ireland there is a very different scheme. There farmers are for the most part small-scale producers with fewer leaders of the type represented in the English National Farmer's Union. Consequently they look more to the government for leadership and a majority of the Board is nominated by the government. In this scheme all milk is compulsorily classified according to its hygienic-quality by four letters. Grades A, B, C are characterized on their containers by the colours green, amber and red. Grade D is not allowed on the liquid market. The higher grades are subsidized partly by levies and partly by a Treasury subsidy. This scheme has proved most successful.

Returning to England and Wales—owing to Parliament having dealt with agriculture piecemeal and to the delay in putting forward any policy for livestock, many farmers changed over to dairying who had not previously produced milk whilst others increased their output, every farmer being assured of getting the pool price for as much as he produced.

The liquid market was unable to absorb this increased supply and as already explained a considerable new industry for dairy products sprang up. This has only been made possible by subsidies; a direct subsidy from the taxpayer, fluctuating with world prices from £1½ million to £2 million, and an indirect subsidy in the form of a concealed levy on milk drinkers which began at 1d. per gallon (totalling £2¾ million) increasing to about 3d. per gallon (or a total of about £9 million) as the factory policy developed, and the volume of milk converted into cheese and butter increased. When the average prices of imported butter and cheese fall, over a period, below a certain level, assistance is given by the Exchequer on a prescribed scale to the Boards in respect of standard gallonages of milk. The aim of this scheme is to safeguard the industry against the effect of any serious fall in the prices of butter and cheese below 1937 levels.

The Milk Board acquired some factories but let private enterprise do most of the business. The policy of subsidizing and so expanding this butter and cheese industry has attracted considerable criticism. New vested interests have been established on the basis of a temporarily increased output of manufacturing milk which these interests will naturally endeavour to perpetuate. Naturally if an industry in milk products is fostered, those associated with it will attempt to keep their business going. It has actually been found in the past that during a winter period vendors of milk had difficulty in getting adequate supplies because of the milk going (under contract) to the factories. The growth of this new industry is perhaps one of the most unfortunate indirect results of the Milk Board's policy. There seems little likelihood of English manufacturers of butter and cheese being able, unaided, to compete with countries like New Zealand where cattle are out-wintered, where grass grows perennially, where fewer expensive fertilizers and concentrates are required, and where the wages bill is lower. It would, owing to the expense, be difficult to justify a policy of increasing by subsidy or import control our domestic production of butter and cheese. Any substantial increase in the price of butter would seriously reduce consumption, and after all this branch is of relatively small importance to farmers. A far more hopeful development is an expansion of milk for consumption as such.

As was shown in the hypothetical case quoted on p. 197 it is not to the farmers' interest to increase the proportion of their total supply which has to be paid for at the lower manufacturing price by expanding the milk products branch of their industry.

Milk Consumption

The average consumption of milk per head is deplorably low, little more than one-third of a pint per day. The serious aspect from the point of view of public health of this low consumption is that it is at its lowest among those with the smallest incomes. Enquiries show that about 25% of unemployed families take no liquid milk at all, whilst in all poor families the average per head instead of increasing actually diminishes with the number of children. In fact the drinking of milk in sufficient quantities is outside the reach of large sections of the population for whom milk is too much of a luxury and not enough of a beverage or food. This need could be met partly if the sale of skim milk were encouraged instead of being prohibited by the Milk Board regulations for, though cheap, it retains most of its valuable minerals and vitamins.

Custom and a curious social prejudice still prevails against milk as a beverage though the recent appearance of "milk bars" in all parts of the country and the educational campaign of the Milk Publicity Council and Milk Boards may effect a minor revolution in our social customs to the very great advantage of the health of the people and of the prosperity of agriculture.

The most obvious method of increasing consumption would be a substantial reduction in price. So far the Milk Boards have pursued a policy of keeping up the cost in the liquid market and selling to manufacturers of milk products what the public will not buy at this high liquid price. They have not attempted to expand consumption by a reduction of price, their avowed policy being that "it is better to produce a little for a lot than a lot for a little."

The Board also have fixed the *retail* price high in order to induce distributors to pay producers higher prices. The Food Council have condemned as unnecessary the big margin between the wholesale and retail prices as did the Cutforth Commission.

Opinions conflict as to the exact effect of price on consumption. It is probable that the response to price reduction might take time to become considerable and that the reduction in price might have to be substantial to have a big effect on consumption. In a recent experiment in four distressed areas where 20,000 persons were eligible milk was sold at half price. It was found as a result that for every 100 pints previously sold at the full price 30 pints were sold at full price and 131 at the reduced rate—an increase in consumption of 61 per cent.

The Milk Board has also co-operated in the Milk-in-Schools Scheme which is partially financed by an Exchequer Subsidy. Children attending elementary schools can obtain one-third of a pint per head per day for $\frac{1}{2}d$. i.e. at half price. Since the institution of the scheme consumption by these children has increased from 9 million to 22 million gallons a year.

These experiments suggest the real scope there is for expanding consumption if substantial price reductions are made. But the Milk Board, being elected by and responsible to dairy farmers, has hesitated to embark on any large scale on a policy which might turn out detrimental to their financial interests. It is unwilling to take this risk. Nor can it, being merely a producers' body, bring pressure to bear for a reduction in their margin on the distributors with whom it has to bargain. Finally, again because it is a Producers' Board, it is unable to make an effective disinterested appeal to the Government to subsidize more extensively the consumption of milk in those classes which need it most.

Re-constitution of the Boards

An efficient system of milk marketing is a matter of the highest public interest. Abolishing the evil consequences of malnutrition, improving the physical, mental and consequently the social well-being will only be attained when milk consumption is greatly increased by a comprehensive national nutrition policy. For this purpose milk should be clean, hygienic, of good quality, and be within the purchasing power of the public. It is difficult to see how the last named object can be reconciled with arrangements which place the determination of the price of milk in the hands of a body exclusively representative of producers. A Producers' Board necessarily tends to give the benefit of any doubt to arguments in favour of a higher price and finds it difficult to impose increased efficiency and modern methods upon its constituents who elect its members.

There is a further argument against a Board consisting almost entirely of producers. Registering all dairy farmers and making them vote annually for the Milk Board has inevitably tended to organize them into a political force. The Milk Board supervises a vast business with a wholesale revenue of over £50 million and with widespread ramifications and contacts and every year spends some £55,000 in press and poster advertising. The powerful political force represented by the Board and its constituents did not hesitate to mobilize and lead an attack which helped to defeat the amending Bill which the Government thought necessary in the interests of the public and the country.

This country should follow the example of Northern Ireland, or adopt the precedent set for Livestock, i.e. an independent Commission, and transform the character of the Milk Marketing Boards from bodies representative of the farmers alone to Boards with at least a majority of other members nominated by the Minister of Agriculture, (for Scotland the Secretary of State for Scotland) in consultation with the Minister of Health. A nominated Board wielding statutory powers and exercising important functions has become in the post-war period a familiar feature of our administration, e.g. the Central Electricity Board, the London Passenger Transport Board, and the B.B.C.

In our judgment the case for changing the Milk Marketing Boards from a purely producer-elected body to one with an independent nominated majority representing the public interest is overwhelming. This view was emphatically shared by the Re-organization Commission.

Problems of Distribution

The question of distribution presents a separate problem from that of production.

Here too there is much room for improvement and economies. This applies first of all to the transport from farm to town. Transport allowances are too high and being uniform regardless of distance, distributors have made a profit on the transport allowance and have obtained milk increasingly from Cumberland, Wales and the West. Consumers have not benefited by any fall in price or elimination of high cost producers. But the biggest scope for improvements is to be found in the transport of milk from the town depot to the consumer's door-step.

Milk is, or should be, a standardized and graded commodity; provided its quality is officially certified it should not matter to the housewife who brings it to her door. The public would suffer little inconvenience if the distribution of milk were so organized that each street or district was served by a single distributor. At present, it is not uncommon to find four, five, six or even ten milkmen serving the same street. This entails waste of labour necessarily reflected in the price paid by the consumer.

Our present statutory control accentuates this waste. The Milk Board have stopped competition and no distributor is allowed to sell milk below the price fixed for his area by the Milk Marketing Board. But each distributor is anxious to attract to himself the largest custom. The distributors compete accordingly with one another by expenditure on canvassing or in similar ways; and this necessarily raises the level of distributive costs. As a result the cost of distribution and distributors' margins have increased. Part of this competitive expenditure is directed, it is true, to the provision of additional service; two deliveries are made per day, milk is supplied in half-pint bottles; which services are convenient to customers. Poorer consumers might however prefer cheaper milk to an elaborate service.

In principle the case for making the retail distribution of milk a monopoly in given areas or of transforming it into a public service is overwhelming. In advocating this step, however, we do not ignore the difficulties. Existing retailers comprise a large variety of types, including the producer-retailer who in certain places fulfils a useful function, large combines whose work of retail distribution is closely associated with their work of wholesale distribution, and the co-operative movement which possesses a peculiar character of its own. Any project for the reorganization of milk distribution is likely to meet strong opposition from these and other interests. This was proved by the agitation against the Milk Bill in December 1938. Events may, however, show that this opposition was short-sighted if existing small retailers are at some future time squeezed out by the bigger organizations without that compensation which the Bill offered them. There is much to be said for local experiments, and we should like to see Local Authorities endowed with powers to retail milk, though not necessarily to the exclusion of private traders.

There are many ways in which a reformed and nominated board or commission could approach the problem of reducing prices, and thus increasing consumption. The Boards might, for example, as has been done with success in Northern Ireland, arrange schemes by which milk would be supplied at cheap rates on a cash-and-carry principle. It would probably also carry more weight with the public and the Government in making recommendations for further subsidies for the provision of cheap or free milk to children, both of school and pre-school age, and to nursing mothers.

Since the adequate supply of milk to children, infants and nursing mothers is the crux of the campaign against malnutrition, as well as being of considerable benefit to agriculture, this is one of the first questions with which a reconstructed Milk Board should deal.

We, therefore, regard the transformation of the composition of the Milk Marketing Boards as a vital and urgently needed reform. There are, indeed, few questions within the sphere of agricultural economics upon which the right line of policy is so clear and the case for it on merits so overwhelming. If an adequate volume of agricultural production is to be maintained in Great Britain, without recourse to high agrarian protection which would be detrimental alike to our standard of living, to our interests as an exporting country and to our national security, the first essential is that our consumption of milk should be steadily and substantially increased. There is a vast untapped market awaiting our farmers, for, if real progress is to be made in improving the nutrition and so the physique, health and welfare of the population, one of the chief needs is an increased consumption of milk by children and nursing mothers. A lower price to the consumer is essential to achieve this object. This requires an improvement in our methods of producing milk, an improvement in our methods of distributing it and the evolution of policy along lines which will place first the interests of the consuming public and the rising generation in particular. At present the constitution of the Milk Marketing Boards blocks the way.

The only objection, indeed, that can be made to the proposal to transform the Milk Marketing Boards is that the change might be shortsightedly opposed by farming interests, as was in fact done in December 1938 when the Milk Board helped to organize opposition to the Milk Bill which the Government introduced to amend the earlier Marketing Act. Political opposition by farming interests must inevitably carry weight. But equally it is a consideration which should not be allowed to dominate our policy and prevent needed reform. The whole trend of agricultural policy in recent years has effected a material improvement in the position of farmers. They have gained both in immediate prosperity and in security against the recurrence of disaster. The assistance given to them has entailed a substantial burden both on the tax-payer and the consuming public. But the public has agreed that in view of the importance of agriculture it is right that this burden should be borne. In return the public has a right to expect that farmers will not obstruct desirable developments of policy by clinging to anomalous privileges, which can neither be justified nor reconciled with the public welfare.

PART FOUR

PERSONNEL AND ORGANIZATION

CHAPTER XVII

THE AGRICULTURAL WORKER

The Rural Exodus

WE have now passed in review the principal products of British agriculture. But the problems of crop production depend not only on circumstances peculiar to these crops but equally on the character of the personnel of the industry and the nature of its general organization. These must in turn be studied. We begin with the agricultural worker.

The history of the agricultural worker has been dominated for the past 80 years by the rural exodus to the towns. In every country of Western Europe the *proportion* engaged in agriculture of the total population has been steadily falling ever since reliable statistics began to be compiled and the same is true of newly developed countries overseas. In Britain, however, industrialization began earlier and so hastened the process. On the whole the exodus has not been disadvantageous to land workers since it led to an advance in wages for those who remained on the land. Faced with the practical impossibility of improving his position, it is not surprising that the countryside was drained of many of its best able-bodied workers—either by emigration or by the prospect of better wages and a more exciting way of living in the industrial towns.

According to the census returns the total number of workers occupied in agriculture had fallen from 1,591,300 in 1881, to 1,198,000 in 1931. Since 1921 the number of adult male workers increased slightly up to 1929, while all other classes show a steep decline; since then, adults have also declined and most significant of all few younger men are coming in to fill the places of the older workers. So, the class of adult workers is coming to consist more and more of elderly men.

Continued migration of the young and enterprising has created a real shortage of skilled workers. For this farmers are in part to blame as in the past they have not offered wages high enough to attract the more able men. In addition the average medium sized farm has not enough opportunity for men to learn modern methods on it. This shortage of skilled workers is important because though to some extent the old skilled occupations—ploughman, thatcher, hedger—are disappearing—the new technique requires a high degree of intelligence and skill.

Farming cannot offer for this work wages comparable with those in industry. Nor are there many farms sufficiently large to have higher posts to which the more talented labourers can rise. There are, it is true, opportunities for energetic labourers to acquire smallholdings and become their own masters, but ordinary promotion, rising to a higher wage-scale, is rare in agriculture. It is this relative absence of real worth-while jobs to rise to, which makes agricultural labour unattractive to many enterprising young men.

There has also been a very substantial decline in female labour. The picturesque milkmaid of other days has given place to the milking-machine. This and the decline of the farm butter and cheese industries have helped to lessen the amount of female labour required in dairying, though numbers are still engaged in other branches.

There has been a noticeable decline in casual labour owing to the increased mechanization of harvesting and other branches of farming and to the operation of unemployment insurance which removes the incentive to do odd jobs. In many cases, however, farmers have found it necessary to create full-time jobs wherever possible, in an effort to prevent labour from moving away. This has been especially noticeable since 1936.

In districts where agriculture has been able to adjust itself to changing world conditions, the exodus has been partly checked, e.g. in Worcestershire, South Lancashire and Middlesex where a large market-garden industry has developed, and in Ayrshire, where a successful dairying industry has been built up, there has been little diminution in the agricultural population.

Wages

Professor Bowley gives the following comparative figures for the average weekly wages of an agricultural labourer and a town labourer in the 19th century; in 1824 these were respectively 6s. 6d. and 16s. 0d.; in 1867, 14s. 0d. and 20s. 0d., and in 1897 16s. 0d. and 25s. 0d. In general, the wages of town labourers were about half as high again and of town artisans twice as high, as those of agricultural labourers.

Coming nearer to our own times,[1] in 1913 the average weekly wages of an agricultural labourer, builder's labourer and bricklayer were respectively, 18s. 0d., 27s. 0d. and 40s. 0d.; in 1924, 28s. 0d., 55s. 6d. and 73s. 5d.; in 1936, 32s. 0d., 52s. 2d. and 69s. 4d.

The relative level of agricultural and industrial wages was about similar in 1936 to what it was a century ago.

Wage regulation began during the war when the cost of living rose more rapidly than wages. In 1918 guaranteed agricultural prices led to a demand for a guaranteed minimum wage. This was introduced with the Corn Production Act which set up a Wages Board. In the 1921 deflation the Act was repealed and Conciliation Committees replaced the Wages Board. This attempt to secure voluntary agreements was a complete failure and it was brought to an end by the Agricultural Wages (Regulations) Act 1924, which still governs agricultural wages. The second National Wages Board was set up with County Committees, who had power to fix minimum wage rates. The level immediately improved, and this increase in money wages was accompanied by a much more rapid increase in real wages which rose by roughly 20 per cent between 1924 and 1936, though the relative advantage of industrial wages remained.

The gap, however, is not so great as comparative figures suggest. Any figure of "average weekly wages" in agriculture must be in some respects misleading. Considerable regional differences exist, due not only to a stronger demand for industrial labour in certain areas but also to

[1] "Abstract of Labour Statistics 1936."

a superior intelligence or competence in agricultural work; for Scotsmen and north-country workers have been migrating south, as they did 50 years ago, because they can command a premium over local labour. By contrast, the lowest rates of wages are paid in certain hill counties of Wales, where no alternative employment exists and the workers are unorganized.

Besides regional differences many agricultural workers take home considerably more in cash than the minimum wage; there are seasonal opportunities for overtime and higher rates for specialized occupations and piecework.

As against this while specialist workers get better wages and general workers earn more than the minimum by overtime and piecework, there are districts where the regulations governing rates of wages are not effectively enforced, in spite of the exhibition of county rates at post offices, an inspectorate and the local workers' union branch. The establishment of unemployment insurance is doing much to remedy this.

A further consideration is the length of the working week in agriculture which compares unfavourably with industry. Standard hours at present range from 48 to 60 per week.

On some farms there is that much-resented institution, the split day—and also the 7-day week. The feeling is growing among agricultural workers that farmers should organize their work to give each man a whole uninterrupted day off per week.

The Cost of Living

Are the low wages of agricultural workers compensated for by a lower cost of living than in the town?

In some respects it is cheaper living in the country. The labourer usually has a garden which keeps him in potatoes and vegetables, he probably also keeps hens and a pig, and, in some districts, wood is available. On the other hand, some commodities are dearer in the village shop than in the town. In recent years the motor-bus and tradesmen's van have helped to reduce this disadvantage. Motor transport has also made possible a reverse movement of vans travelling to rural areas, but these may encourage buying on credit. It is probable that if exactly the same commodities were brought these would cost slightly more in the country than in the town; but tastes and requirements of country workers differ from those of town workers, and on balance their satisfaction involves less expenditure.

In the matter of rent, the countryman gets a substantial advantage; this advantage is often negatived by the quality of the accommodation. Rural housing is one of the most neglected features of our rehousing campaign since the war. Under the Rural Workers' Housing Act (1926) the Government gives grants for the reconditioning of cottages, and under the Housing Act (1930) subsidies are given to Rural District Councils for approved new houses. Under the Overcrowding Act of 1935, 41,928 houses in rural areas were scheduled as overcrowded. Grants are also made for better water supplies; and electricity is coming into the village; too often conditions are still deplorable especially in water supplies and drainage.

The "tied" cottage is another grievance of the agricultural worker. These are cottages which "go with the job"; and loss of the job means loss to the worker of a roof over his head. Where the worker is engaged on a weekly basis this insecurity of tenure is keenly felt, and there is little chance of redress if the cottage is bad.

The above considerations show that most labourers' cottages suffer from a number of serious drawbacks which counterbalance cheap rents.

Nevertheless living in the country has many important compensating advantages. Farm work, in spite of long hours and weather conditions, is healthier than much industrial and office work. It satisfies the desire for creative activity in a way that repetition of a mechanical operation does not.

In addition the motor-cycle, motor-bus and radio have done much to reduce the sense of isolation, and in the village itself there is a greater diversity of activities than formerly.

In the last 7–8 years adult education classes have spread to quite a remarkable extent. One Midland University institution runs well over a hundred courses of varying lengths in the neighbouring countryside. There are the Rural Community Committees, which generally run the activities of the village hall, where there may be a County Library branch. For women, there is the Women's Institute, with its 5,000 branches scattered over every county, bringing women of every class together in friendly social contact. The Queen's Institute of District Nursing now provides an essential service in every corner of Britain.

None the less there can be no doubt that to the bulk of the young people in the country the economic advantages and other attractions of town life outweigh the advantages both actual and intangible of life in the country. Realizing this, even more conscious effort should be made to strengthen the position of the landworker.

Improvement in Status

On the side of the workers this has been developed through trade unionism. The difficulties of organizing workers scattered over wide areas are enormous and unionism has never embraced as much as 50 per cent, at times being as low as 5 per cent. But if there had been no trade union organization in 1924, it would have been impossible to work satisfactorily the Agricultural Wages Committees. Organizers sit on the committees and protect the workers' interests for it is the trade union organizer who generally forwards complaints of under-payment to the committees, investigates their compensation claims, and settles, often out of court, their legal disputes.

The status of agricultural workers has also been improved by the Unemployment Insurance (Agriculture) Act which came into force in 1936. Before that Act, there were counties in which a land worker with family, who could get an insured job in town, would receive more as an unemployed industrial worker than he would as an employed agricultural worker. It is too soon yet to draw any reliable conclusions as to the effect the scheme is likely to have in the agricultural industry. But the first year's operations showed remarkably low rates of unemployment as compared with other industries—5·6 per cent in January 1937, and 2·7 per cent in July of the same year.

Future Policy

In the past the rural community has had inadequate public services, partly because it has been ill-organized for presenting its claims, and partly because such services are more expensive where the population is scattered. But it is clearly desirable to provide, for the whole population, similar standards in essential services so far as this can be done at reasonable cost.

As one contribution towards this end, we should like to see a far more generous subsidy to rural housing. The only solution is to subsidize rural re-housing, if necessary, more than in the case of municipal housing schemes, so that the land worker can enjoy good housing for a sum not greatly in excess of what he pays at present.

Far more active steps should be taken to encourage local authorities to provide minimum standards of water supplies to villages in the interest of public health. In a country with such a rainfall as ours it is paradoxical and a scandal that in so many villages water should have to be carried long distances to individual houses, and that in some districts there is an actual scarcity nearly every summer.

There is much room for improvement in education facilities, and in order that the Primary Schools may have similar advantages to Central Schools we would support a policy of reorganizing them into larger units covering wider areas, and giving in them a better education than has hitherto been possible. Already some counties bring children from outlying districts to school by motor-bus, and this practice should be more generally adopted.

Besides general education, it is desirable to provide more technical training for those going into agriculture, and for the young worker already on a farm. Though practical experience is no doubt the best training, the application of the latest methods requires specific knowledge which there is not ordinarily an opportunity to learn on the farm. We should like to see a much more comprehensive scheme for instructional courses for farm workers. This would probably need to be organized in various ways. In some cases it could become one of the activities of Farm Institutes. Reorganization on these lines should create senior posts to which trained workers can rise.

The rural exodus is, however, likely to continue; indeed, in view of the change now going on in the age-distribution of the agricultural population, whereby the labour corps is composed increasingly of middle-aged and elderly workers, it is certain that the exodus will become much more rapid in the near future. Many people regret this urbanization and point to evils of a psychological kind which seem to result from a lack of contact with nature. But however great are the values contributed by a rural community to the national life we cannot be content to preserve it at a permanently lower standard of living. From this point of view too, an improved standard is desirable.

Finally, it is a mistake to assume that if some labour leaves agriculture, therefore the fabric of village life will collapse. Village life is changing but it is not disintegrating. During the last twenty years there has grown up a greater variety of occupations and activities in the village. In some, new light industries, using electricity, have been established. The growth of motoring has also created new village occupations. On the social side, too, as explained, there is a general participation in the organization of all sorts of activities, and far less dependence on the "Big House". A healthy village community will not be one composed of a mass of low-paid labourers looking to those above them for initiative and leadership. It will be one composed of persons engaged in a wide variety of occupations, who are prepared to take an increasing share in the life of their district. In this sense, rural society is developing a diversity greater than ever previously possessed.

CHAPTER XVIII

SMALLHOLDERS·

THERE is probably no other aspect of the land question which has attracted so much discussion, and on which such widely divergent views have been held, as the problem of smallholdings. Whenever the rural exodus has been particularly marked, or whenever industrial unemployment has been severe, the question has come up.

Taking the statutory definition of a smallholding as "a farm of less than 50 acres or of less than £100 annual rental value", there are probably about 134,000 smallholdings in Great Britain. Although the smallholders produce no more than one-sixth of our food, they maintain nearly half the total number of farm families. They consist partly of persons who cultivate their holdings as part time occupations, partly of retired persons, perhaps with small pensions, partly of ex-farmers, trying to supplement their incomes. But a large number of smallholders depend on their holdings for their livelihood.

It is these latter whom the State has been trying to increase. Small-Holding Acts were passed in 1892, 1908, 1919 and 1926, and in all counties of England and Wales, the County Councils have, to a greater or lesser extent, prepared schemes totalling some 30,000 holdings in thirty years, more than one-fifth of all the smallholdings in existence. These Council schemes have never been entirely self-supporting, especially not in 1919-1926 when ex-service men were put on the land. Up to 1926 the State bore the burden of loss on smallholdings amounting to £7–£8 millions, about £250 per holding. Since then, the County Councils have shouldered the risk, but few new smallholdings have been created. During the depression of 1930–35, renewed interest was shown in smallholdings, and a Land Settlement Association was formed to settle unemployed industrial workers on the land.

What are the possibilities of settling large numbers on the land ? How, in fact, are existing smallholders faring ? What are their difficulties and how do they overcome them ? What are the factors leading to success or failure ? With a view to answering these questions, we undertook in 1935 an investigation into the economic conditions of small-holders in widely different districts. Our conclusions were published in " The Agricultural Dilemma " and were dis-appointing to those of us who had placed high hopes on extensive land settlement, so we continued our enquiry. With the co-operation of agricultural economists in different parts of the country, we collected a considerable body of information, constituting probably the most extensive and detailed account of the conditions of smallholdings which has yet been collected in this country. We set out in this chapter a summary of the conclusions to which this material has led us.

In the first place, it is well to be clear as to the purposes which smallholdings are designed to serve. There are first, the smallholdings run as a part time occupation, by persons with other sources of income ; they are about 15–20 per cent of the total number of holdings.

Another type is the smallholding run as a full-time occupation. Here the smallholders may be using the holding as a step in the agricultural ladder to large-scale farming, accumulating experience and savings on the way ; or they may simply desire to be their own masters, and are willing to work long hours to reap an extremely small reward.

It is with the man to whom the smallholding is a full-time job that we are mainly concerned. What has been the measure of his success in the various branches of agriculture into which his enterprise has led him ?

Fruit and Market-Gardening

According to the Ministry of Agriculture Census for 1930, there were 13,670 fruit and vegetable holdings in England and Wales. Our enquiries referred mainly to the small 3–10 acres holding and revealed a uniformly unfavourable tale of results. In Hampshire the standard of living was little better than that of a hired labourer. In Devonshire there was virtually no demand for the 3–10 acres market-garden. In the Evesham and Pershore district the condition of the smaller grower was pitiable. Among seventy-one visited, hardly one was in any sense prosperous and many had to take casual jobs on neighbouring farms to make ends meet. In Yorkshire, of the various types of small holding visited, the market-gardens were the least successful.

What were the main reasons for the failure of the market-garden holdings? Briefly, they are as below :—

(1) Firstly comes the intense competition of the large farms with their elaborate machinery of cultivation. How can a smallholder hope to compete with a farm using a machine which can plant 80,000 cabbages a day? These big farms can work on a profit margin of £1 an acre, whereas the smallholder on 3–5 acres needs £20–£30 profit per acre for a fair living.

(2) Difficulties of marketing reduce vegetable and fruit growing almost to a gamble. Frequently the smallholder after sending his produce to the market had been informed, either that it had been unsold, or sold for little or nothing, and, in some cases, had resulted in an actual loss owing to cost of carriage and postage. This, in many cases, is inherent in the market-gardening business; the output of small gardens is too small for satisfactory grading, and the smallholder, being unorganised, has rarely adequate market information.

(3) The difficulty in getting ideal soil and climate often results in failure.

(4) "Rents" was often alluded to by individual small-holders, but even a considerable reduction in rent would

not, in most cases, have meant the difference between success and failure. In intensive enterprises of this kind rent is not a burdensome item in costs.

(5) Possession of capital is of paramount importance. In the old days it was possible to build up a small reserve by putting aside savings, but to-day intense competition has reduced the chances.

(6) The size of the holding is an important factor, but exactly what size was desirable varied in different districts. In Evesham they said 5 acres is the "one-man" limit. But in Pershore one man could manage 10–12 acres. In Scotland 8 acres were considered inadequate for a successful small market-garden. In Hampshire smallholders complained of insufficient acreage; they wanted to keep pigs and poultry as a secondary enterprise. There is no doubt that some livestock, when practicable, improves the position of the market-garden holder, providing him with manure and another source of income.

Poultry-holdings

Smallholders who specialized in poultry in England and Wales, according to the statistics for 1930, numbered only 4,927; except in Lancashire they do not congregate in particular areas. We found a wide variety of economic circumstances among them. Some were in a hopeless state of despair, others were just making ends meet, while a few appeared extremely prosperous.

There were two types of poultry-holders who appeared to make a success: those who specialized in the sale of hatching eggs and young stock, and those with the larger flocks. A flock of less than 400–500 birds does not provide full time employment for one man, and will not provide him with a living. In general poultry flocks on mixed farms proved more profitable than those on holdings devoted exclusively to poultry keeping. When poultry were run on mixed farms, less was spent on feeding-stuffs, less on hatching eggs and young stock, and less on equipment. But this raises special difficulties.

The small poultry-holder suffers from two disadvantages, the fluctuations in the price of imported feeding-stuffs, (on which success mainly depends) and the liability of poultry to sudden visitations of disease. Poultry keeping is so risky an enterprise as to be hardly well-suited to smallholders. A risky business requires capital to provide against bad times.

Dairy-holdings

Taken as a whole, this was in all districts far the most successful group of smallholders. There are many reasons for the prosperity of the dairy-holding.

Much of the labour needed in milk production can be done part time by women and girls; the smallholder with a wife and family has considerable advantages over the farmer who has to hire labour.

The smallholder can also give more personal attention to the individual cows than can the small farmer with his mass-production methods. Lastly, milk production is a 7-day a week job, which the larger farmer can only get done by paying overtime. And the dairy smallholder enjoys a further advantage, among all other kinds of small-holder, of having an assured market for his produce, through the establishment of the Milk Marketing Board. If, however, more stringent requirements are enacted for ensuring the cleanliness and safety of our milk, necessitating concrete flooring, sterilizing equipment, with stricter veterinary inspection, the smallholder may find himself at a disadvantage.

There are two essentials to success in dairy-holding; the holding must not be too small. The evidence of our surveys suggests that higher profits were associated with the larger holding. Secondly, the herd should be as large as the holding can conveniently carry. Situation does not appear to be a decisive factor. Successful dairy-holders were found on all kinds of soil. But proximity to markets is important wherever the smallholder wants to retail his milk. The producer-retailer was generally found to be the most successful of the dairy smallholders; this is particularly so where he has the assistance of his family in working the rounds. He will, however, have to reckon with less secure advantages in future. He will have to follow the practice of bottling, which will involve him in additional expense. And the intensification of competition among milk distributors has led to an increase in the services offered to consumers, which the small producer-retailer will find it difficult to undertake.

Mixed Arable Holdings

There are not many smallholders of this type; they include innumerable combinations of farm enterprise—field crops, potatoes, sugarbeet, livestock, milk and eggs.

The advantage of the mixed small holding is that it is less affected by fluctuations in the price of one particular product, and it may produce a wide range of food stuffs which can support almost the entire family in times of distress. But in the majority of cases it affords an extremely low standard of living. In good times it will yield the small-holder little more than the wages of an agricultural labourer, in bad times substantially less. On the whole these holdings are looked upon primarily as a training ground; as a rung in the agricultural ladder, they possess the great advantage of providing experience in different farm enterprises, and for this reason alone a certain number will always be in demand. At the same time, they provide such a narrow income that occupiers are constantly endeavouring to graduate to some larger farm which can be more economically managed.

Mixed Pasture Holdings

These are found mostly in the hilly areas of our Western Counties. The principal enterprise in most cases is the rearing of store cattle or store sheep with usually some sale of milk, eggs or pigs. Few have been created by the County Councils; rather they are a natural part of the farming system of the West. The demand for these holdings comes mainly from agricultural labourers or the sons of small-scale farmers. Most of the holdings surveyed were of 30-acres and upwards. Many of these holdings rear a part of the stock which replenishes the beef and dairy herds of England, the unsatisfactory quality of much of this stock is largely due to the lack of capital and sometimes to the ignorance of many people in the cattle-raising industry. The small-scale producers cannot often afford pedigree bulls, and except in parts of Scotland, are generally unwilling to come together in cattle breeding societies. As long as the rearing industry remains so largely in the hands of small farmers, and even of smallholders, progress in improving the quality of live-stock must inevitably be slow.

General Considerations

The experience of the various authorities concerned in the creation and administration of smallholdings, points to definite conclusions on policy.

Firstly, how far is it desirable for a prospective small-holder to have had previous experience in agriculture? A sample analysis of 1,180 County Council smallholders showed that nearly two-thirds had previously been in agricultural occupations, and that only 10 per cent came from urban occupations. Most County Councils insist on previous agricultural experience, though in some cases it is conceded that general business ability may be even more useful than a technical knowledge of agricultural operations. It is probably true that ex-urban workers contribute the few outstanding successes amongst small-holders, owing chiefly to their business mentality, but this is more than counter-balanced by the high proportion of failures. The agricultural applicants provide the steady tenants.

A second point is, that the smallholder should have a country, and not an urban outlook; there can be no trade union hours; pleasures and hobbies must be "the holding".

H

One of the most successful men visited had never taken a holiday, never been to a cinema, a music-hall or a theatre. Thirdly, the holder must have had not merely agricultural experience, but agricultural experience of the right kind. It is no use having learned the technique of extensive farming and trying to carry it out on a 50-acre farm. Several of the least successful holdings were in the hands of men who had previously been workers or foremen on large farms and could not adapt themselves to conditions of intensive farming.

On the question of the age of smallholders it was found from an analysis made in Scotland, that the unsuccessful settlers were on the average rather younger than the successful, and that fewer of them were married. The older family man proved the more reliable type of settler.

There is an important qualification to success in smallholding, namely, to have learned the value of thrift, so that the farm capital may be augmented out of savings. Often the failure of ex-urban workers was due to lack of petty thrift. Capital is essential to success.

A final consideration is the equipment needed on a smallholding. In the early days of smallholdings (1909–14) nearly half of those created were "bare-land" units, i.e., without dwelling house or farm buildings. To-day, the bulk of the demand is for fully equipped buildings. This is partly related to the change in the size and type of holding demanded. In several counties the small "bare-land" holdings have become difficult to re-let, and have had to be amalgamated so as to create one fully equipped 40–50 acre holding.

The difficulties of smallholders in making a financial success are increased by the cost of time and money involved in marketing their produce, by the cost in purchasing fertilisers in small quantities, and by the inability to provide suitable sires and breeding stock. These difficulties could be largely eliminated if the holdings were associated with a processing factory, a central buying office and a farm where suitable bulls, boars and breeding stock were kept.

To keep processing factories would probably require the output of some 10,000 acres of about 200 smallholdings. If an experiment on these lines were initiated the factories and breeding stock might also be available for farmers on larger holdings in the district. The central unit could probably be run even more economically if it were associated with 20,000 acres, viz, half smallholdings and half ordinary farms. Such a unit need not be in a ring fence, nor should smallholders be compelled to utilise the processing factories. Obviously such a scheme would in certain cases have to ignore county boundaries. A unit on these lines, capable of adaption and variation, should increase the opportunity necessary for smallholders' prosperity.

We may now summarize the general conclusions to which our surveys have led us.

All the evidence suggests that market-gardening holdings are the least successful type at present. Poultry-keeping on a small scale is too risky an enterprise for smallholders with present widespread disease and violent fluctuation in the price of feeding-stuffs. Nevertheless, there is a place for small horticultural and poultry holdings. Many of those which already exist will undoubtedly continue to provide their occupiers with a modest, and in a few instances, even a comfortable living. But there is unlikely to be any strong demand among new applicants for holdings of this kind.

The dairy smallholdings appear to be in a favourable economic position, mainly due to the general relative prosperity of the milk industry, and to the efforts of the Milk Marketing Board's price policy. Future prospects are less hopeful. As standards of hygiene in milk production are raised, the dairy smallholder will find his position increasingly difficult in competition with the big distributor. The public demands clean and safe milk. The dairy smallholder is the producer least well able to meet these requirements.

Mixed holdings, whether of the arable or pasture type, generally provide only a meagre living, unless the land happens to be suited to some more lucrative crop, such as sugar-beet or potatoes.

But in order that mixed and dairy holdings shall have the best possible chance of success, it is desirable that they should be of a size somewhat larger than a statutory small-holding, and that they should be equipped with adequate buildings. This means that to create new holdings is an expensive undertaking, amounting to some £2,000 to £3,000 per man settled; often the rent which can be charged only suffices to cover a portion, perhaps half, of the maintenance costs plus loan-interest, and repayment charges. This consideration in itself renders impracticable any sudden and considerable increase.

There remains the question of the provision by County Councils of part-time holdings. To this activity no strictly economic principles can be applied. The requirements are quite different from those of full-time holdings. Generally, a small acreage unequipped with house or buildings, will suffice. The holder who specializes, perhaps in poultry, or even vegetables, may earn a useful addition to his income, even in his spare time. The part-time holder may also acquire in this way a taste for farming which may induce him to take a full-time holding later on. For others with no such ambitions, it is desirable to provide a healthy spare-time occupation, which also supplements the family's diet in the winter in the health-protective foods. In this sense, the County Councils' work in providing part-time holdings has real value.

In general, we favour a cautious continuation of the County Councils' Smallholdings' policy along the present lines. The system has worked in the main satisfactorily; the statistics show that small holdings do serve useful purposes and do contribute something of value to the life of the rural community. On the other hand, in the light of the evidence we have obtained, it is impossible to advocate any wide extension of smallholding schemes though apparently in Scotland there is still an unsatisfied demand. The future will, undoubtedly, be less rather than more friendly

to smallholders. We have noted trends which indicate
that British agriculture is becoming more mechanised,
more highly capitalised, and more devoted to producing
high-quality foodstuffs in bulk. These trends are all
inimical to the success of small-scale producers. In consequence there can be no wisdom in incurring substantial
fresh liabilities by the creation of a large number of new
smallholdings.

CHAPTER XIX

FARMERS

THE characteristic features of our farming industry are the varied extent of its enterprises and the wide diversity of interests, skill and social status among those responsible for its control and management. There are so many different categories of farmers working under special conditions of soil and climate, with their own specific problems and difficulties, that generalisations are impossible. All we can do is to examine their actual position and prospects in the light of present-day world conditions.

We may divide farmers into three groups. First, the substantial farmer, with 150–500 or 600-acres, employing labour but usually undertaking the management himself. Above this group there are still larger farms where managerial duties are delegated to a steward or manager. Secondly, we have farmers with smaller farms, say, 50-150 acres, generally worked by the farmer and members of his family, but sometimes with the help of one or two hired workers, to which type of farm is usually given the name of "family farm". Both these groups are usually mixed farms. Finally, comes the smallholder spoken of in the preceding chapter.

There are approximately 300,000 persons describing themselves as farmers, 250,000 in England and Wales and 75,000 in Scotland (including crofters). Their numbers have remained remarkably stable in the last 60 years. This total may be divided amongst the three groups as follows: 55,000 in the 150-acres and over group; 110,000 in the 50-150-acres group; and 134,000 in the group with under 50-acres.

The 55,000 medium and large-scale farmers cultivate

half the total acreage but produce rather less than half of the total agricultural output. They grow the bulk of British wheat and barley, and undertake the major part of the bullock fattening. They are found mostly in the Midland and Western counties. They employ half the total number of agricultural workers—roughly an average of 6-7 per farm. Their average gross output ranges between £1,500 and £3,000 or £30–£60 per week, which roughly, represents the sales of a medium-sized suburban shop. On the other hand, there is far more capital engaged in such a farm than in a shop—say, £6,000 or more, of which in cases where the occupier rents his farm, about a third belongs to the tenant. The income of the majority of these farms will usually range between £200 and £800 a year. Of course, there are farmers whose incomes fall outside these limits.

It is particularly men in this group who take active part in public affairs, who combine in farmers' organizations, and develop into leaders of the farmer-politician class. They exercise a preponderant influence on County Councils; they sit on agricultural committees and wages committees, and their national leaders work strenuously for the agricultural interest, both inside and outside Parliament.

The 110,000 of "family farms" are found in all districts. They employ about 200,000 workers, an average of nearly two a farm, including relatives of the farmer. The capital invested in such a farm will range around £3,000 (roughly speaking, two-thirds landlord's, and one-third tenant's; though, of course, landlord and tenant are sometimes the same person). And the gross annual output may be between £500 and £1,500. The income of these farmers is usually between £100 and £300 a year, including the value of produce and rental value of the house.

The outstanding economic advantage of the "family farm" consists in its supply of cheap labour. Neither the farmer nor his son, working with him, demands a full cash wage. They are both prepared, if need be, to take no more than their keep, which gives them great powers of resistance in periods of depression, and enables them in better times, to devote all their surplus receipts to building up the farm organization.

There is a certain element of shifting in the agricultural community, that is to say, of farmers moving from one farm to another. But this movement appears to be surprisingly small, probably no more than 5 per cent of the total number of farms changing hands each year. One would have expected a movement towards the concentration of farms in the hands of those having a peculiar aptitude for the business. The personal factor showing skill and enterprise even under adverse circumstances seems to be decisive. Yet farms tend to remain in the same family, only changing hands rarely, and there have been few perceptible signs of the more able farmers obtaining control of a larger share of the industry.

Diversity of Qualities

Probably few callings require such a wide range of abilities as that of farming. The farmer should have practical knowledge of most of the manual work about the farm. He should have a certain amount of technical training and a little knowledge of chemistry, biology and engineering; for although he cannot keep abreast of the latest scientific developments in all the different branches of farming, he needs to know when and where he should seek advice, and what the possibilities are of improving his farm equipment and organization. He should be capable of keeping simple accounts. He should have organizing ability. He should be able to distribute the work of the farm through the year, and also geographically over his fields, so as to utilize to best advantage the farm staff, the buildings, the machinery, the livestock and the land itself. He should have qualities of leadership if he is to get the best from his employees; of astuteness towards those with whom he has business transactions; he should have a gift for sensing the right moments for buying and have an eye for a good bargain; he should have a capacity for following those general economic trends which affect the markets, and for planning his farm's production in accordance with world conditions.

In most farms, especially the larger ones, the necessity for careful planning ahead (perhaps for two or three years) for every branch of the farm, is required. Such planning requires exceptional skill and foresight. The necessary complement to budgeting is account-keeping. Recently account-keeping has increased rapidly though even now its value is not universally realized. Indeed, many farmers have a rooted mistrust of book-keeping. They say that a Profit and Loss Account bears little relation to what the farmer feels his position to be. Accounts might show him to be making a loss year after year, whilst still in business and living quite comfortably. Many items, such as the remuneration for labour and management, or the great fluctuation in capital valuation from year to year, cannot be assessed on the arbitrary basis demanded of ordinary accountancy. What accounts can show, however, is how the "budget" has been realized in practice, and how the internal organization of the farm compares in efficiency with other similar farms. Inadequate book-keeping, or the entire absence of it, is mostly found among the smaller farmers, where the farmer himself shares in the work of the farm, and has not the time, and in some cases, not the knowledge either, to make up books at the close of a long day's work. For this reason, the large farm which can afford to employ a book-keeper and is run more consciously on a business basis, will always stand a greater chance of success than the small one.

Farming being an art, skill in valuation and ability to get the maximum out of the factors of production are essential qualifications. The gift of sizing up correctly the qualities of an animal, expertness in the buying of store stock, feeding-stuffs and fertilizers, and, what is perhaps of as great importance, intelligent anticipation of the future course of prices, may make all the difference between profit and loss.

In general, it would appear as if a quite unreasonably large array of qualities and faculties is required in a successful farmer. There are some who possess these qualities in a high degree, but naturally, they are few. The majority are inevitably ordinary persons with no outstanding capabilities, farming indifferently, and only obtaining a mediocre reward for their labour. The question may be asked, then, why do not the more able and gifted farmers concentrate larger portions of the industry in their own hands? Why have not the weaker and less capable ones been driven out, leaving agriculture organized in fewer big units? And if this has not happened, ought not the State to assist in bringing it about? Are farms, on the whole, too small, and could more economic and efficient production be achieved by re-grouping in larger units? Should the State intervene to facilitate the development of large-scale farming?

The Question of Farm Sizes

The most noteworthy feature of British farms has been the measure of stability in their average size. Since 1895 there have been slight increases in the number of holdings in the size-groups 50–100 acres, and 100–150 acres. The only pronounced change has been a reduction of 25 per cent in the holdings of 300-acres and upwards up to 1932, although since then the number of such farms has shown a slight increase. Apart from this, farms seem to have remained very much the same size as they were 40 years ago. What is the explanation?

The size of the farm is dictated to a large extent by the size of the farm buildings, which in most parts of the country are a carry-over from the days of the old arable system when the work was done by horse-teams and simple reaping-machines. To create larger farm units suited to modern mechanized methods or to a large livestock unit would mean considerable reconstruction of the buildings and change in the farm layout, and this would involve heavy initial capital expenditure, which might or might not be covered by the advantages of large-scale production.

A considerable obstacle to the expansion of a farm is of a physical kind. An industrial concern can add another storey to its factory or build a new wing. A farmer who wishes to expand his business wants adjacent land which is rarely to be had. Two-thirds of our agricultural land is in the hands of tenant farmers. The landlord may either have a sitting tenant on the adjacent land whom he is unwilling to evict, or, if the farm does fall vacant, he will usually prefer to have five or six medium-sized tenant farmers to one or two very large ones, if only for the reason that there are more prospective tenants with small rather than large capital. The result is that a farmer unable to acquire an adjacent farm, is often forced to take one some distance away with consequent loss in economy. None of these obstacles need be insuperable. It would be quite feasible, for example, for a company to buy up a whole estate and run it as a single farm, if large-scale farming were really so efficient as to yield an attractive return on capital.

This leads on to the question whether larger units would, in fact, be more profitable than the present ones? In considering this question, people are too apt to have in mind the analogies of the big industrial amalgamations, where the extra administrative costs involved may be offset by substantial economies in other directions. In agriculture, on the other hand, the administrative costs of extra foremen and managers may be extremely high in relation to output, partly due to the mere physical extension of farm operations; it may take the whole of one man's time to supervise as few as 20 labourers working on different jobs in different fields. To offset this, what economies can, in fact, be reasonably anticipated in large-scale production?

Large farmers can obtain their requisites—feeding-stuffs, fertilizers, etc. at cheaper rates, but probably no more cheaply than any medium-sized farmer can. As regards the marketing of produce, there is probably a clear advantage in turning out products like fruit and vegetables on a large scale. But for some products, such as milk and sugar-beet, the price is fixed by a national contract, while for others, such as fatstock, sale is customarily made in small lots. In the matter of rent, large farms would save considerably, since there would be fewer buildings per acre, but the cost of the re-grouping and reconstruction of buildings would have to be met before this economy was felt.

A more important consideration is the effective use of the modern implements and machines necessary in farming to-day. Probably farms of between 200–300 acres at least, are essential for their most profitable employment. Farmers with smaller acreage are, in general, unable to make enough use of their equipment. The layout of the irregularly-shaped small farms adds to costs. Probably, a great deal of the light land of this country could be more efficiently worked in larger fields and larger farm units.

Since our agriculture is primarily concerned with live-stock, an important question is whether larger units will have obvious and substantial advantages in dairying, and cattle-raising. Clearly big economies can be effected by haymaking on a large scale. Clearly too, if grass-drying is to become a commercial proposition, it will be most economically operated for a large unit of grass-land. Apart from this, however, the mechanical appliances used, for instance in milk production, do not require such large farm units as does the machinery used in crop production. A milking-machine can be operated economically by a man and a boy for a herd of 50–60 cows. The "Hosier" open-air system requires a unit of some 60–70 cows. A herd of this size does not involve a particularly large farm. It could well be accommodated on any of the medium-sized farms which are found all over the country at the present time.

There is, however, one distinct disadvantage in specializing in one product on a medium-sized farm. Many of the products from mixed husbandry are not available, and the economic utilization of by-products must be reckoned one of the biggest factors in agricultural efficiency.

In the matter of labour, the small "family farm" is very often in a position to effect economies which offset the technical disadvantages of small-scale production. The farmer and his son who work in the fields get into closer personal relationship with the few men who may be employed, and will get better work out of them. It is difficult to estimate the value of such subtle factors, but they undoubtedly go far to account for the remarkable persistence of family holdings.

We have seen some of the more formidable obstacles to the expansion of farms into large-scale agricultural organizations. Rather than face these difficulties, many enterprising farmers seek to devote their energies to subsidiary businesses, e.g., mechanical farm inventions, breakfast cereal manufacture; or they may develop into dealers or auctioneers, or they may undertake road transport, or go into partnership with wholesale merchants.

The final question arises, how far could the organization of farming be made more efficient? Is there a particular change which would benefit agriculture as a whole? At present, the industry is composed of several hundred thousand units, most of them relatively small, most of them without modern equipment. Would it pay to combine these into larger units, to pursue a policy of amalgamation of holdings?

From the technical point of view we have found a strong case for larger farms which can afford up to date methods in production and marketing. Larger farms would give scope for more scientific management, and would have management posts important enough to attract men of ability. But in practice, serious obstacles, as we have seen, stand in the way of change; these include the system of land tenure, the configuration of land itself, and the costs of amalgamation.

It is obvious then that any wholesale change would be both impracticable and uneconomic. Nevertheless, we believe that in many districts, agriculture would benefit by a gradual regrouping of farms into larger units and we

would like to see a move made in this direction. We
recommend experiments in large-scale farming by private
enterprise and by public authorities in suitable localities;
for if these were carried out over a sufficient period of
time, they might well prove successful beyond anticipation.
Furthermore, the State should, wherever possible, pursue
a policy of facilitating a natural amalgamation of holdings
where this is desired by the farmers themselves. In this
connection the Land Commissions we shall propose could
help. Finally, although we recognize that change will
come slowly, we are convinced that only when farming
is run in rather larger units, will it be possible to secure
a sufficient number of able managers, each with expert
knowledge in his particular department, and also a sufficient
supply of really skilled workers who will be keen and able
to carry out, in day-to-day farm operations, the practical
application of the new technique.

CHAPTER XX

AGRICULTURAL CREDIT

Credit Legislation

THE question of ready credit facilities has long been a difficulty with the agriculturist when he wants to raise money, either for long or short terms. The difficulty lies in the nature and legal status of the security which he can offer for loans. Most of his real wealth is of an insufficiently durable nature to be acceptable to a bank as security. At any rate, the bankers have not shown any particular enthusiasm in their advances to agriculture on short-term loans. In 1922 the total value of farm crops and livestock was estimated at £400 million, and the value of agricultural land at a substantially higher figure, whilst in 1923 a loan census of the Five Big Banks revealed that they had lent only £46½ million to agriculture of which £26 million was for land purchases and the remainder was all that was lent on short-term.

The State has accordingly felt itself obliged to intervene with assistance, and a series of Acts have been passed to secure, by means of the formation of companies, the making of loans for agricultural purposes on favourable terms.

Under the Land Improvement Acts (1864–99) facilities were created through an organization called The Land Improvement Company, for giving loans repayable over 40 years, for the improvement of farms. In 1920 the Farmers' Land Purchase Company was formed to assist tenant farmers to purchase their holdings on long-term credits, and the Agricultural Credits Act of 1928 led to the formation of the Agricultural Mortgage Corporation, whose principal business was lending money on mortgages on agricultural land, either for purchase or major improvements of the land. These also were long-term loans. Certain subsidies, and contributions towards the expenses of the Corporation were to be made by the Exchequer.

The question of the provision of short-term credits to farmers, in the ordinary way of their business, presented much more difficulty to Governments, and has not yet been satisfactorily solved. Reference need only be made to two of the most recent efforts in this direction. The first was the Agricultural Credits Act of 1923, the object of which was the setting up of a system of co-operative credit among farmers, themselves. They were invited to form Societies under the Industrial and Provident Societies Acts, each member of which would take so many £1 shares on which only 5s. need be paid up. The State undertook to advance half the capital of the Society, to be secured by a floating charge on all the assets, including the uncalled capital. In other words, the uncalled capital of members who had not taken loans or had not taken them to the fullest amount of their uncalled capital, could be requisitioned for the repayment of State advances in the event of a borrower defaulting. Actually, only nine societies registered, of which three never started operations.

The State tried again with the Agricultural Credits Act of 1928. The banks were now brought into the scheme. The Act enabled a farmer to create, in favour of his bank, a charge, called an "agricultural charge", on his farming stock and other agricultural assets, as security for an overdraft or for any sum to be paid for him under a guarantee by the bank. These charges had to be registered and a bank holding one ranked as a secured creditor with priority over all unsecured claims.

These Agricultural Charges were very much of the same nature as Bills of Sale which farmers frequently had to resort to for raising money. But they had a profound mistrust of both the bill of sale and the agricultural Charge, and for the same reason, the necessity for public registration. Publication generally brought demands from all the other creditors of the farmer. The Act tried to make the charges system more palatable by not insisting on publication in the newspapers but instead by registration in London, available for inspection only on application. But merchants had no difficulty in keeping themselves informed of these charges through their trade associations, The depression came soon after the Act was launched, and the scheme has been a failure.

Other Methods

All these schemes failed chiefly because they were not sufficiently associated with the methods of farmers. A scheme has been tried out in the Midlands recently, which is more in line with farmers' practices and has probably therefore, greater possibilities in it. A company which runs a livestock market, arranges with a farmer who requires credit for his purchases in the ring, that he need only pay 15 per cent of the full price at the time of purchase. The other 85 per cent plus interest for the accommodation, is payable at some agreed date later. All details of the loan, repayment and delivery of stock, are contained in an agreement which the creditor lodges with the bank. This system brings together the banks' supply of credit with the auctioneer's knowledge of the farmer's financial position. But clearly, it does not eliminate the middleman, who cannot be expected to lose on the transaction. In practice, it is a kind of hire-purchase system for machinery, cattle or other capital goods. It would not often be employed in the case of goods which were immediately consumable.

Numerous other proposals for credit facilities continue to be put forward from time to time—agricultural banks, public-utility credit corporations, and so forth. It is difficult to say how a new loan institution would be able to provide better facilities for farmers. Either it would lend at current rates of interest and insist on adequate security, or it would make a loss and require a subsidy from the Exchequer. As for the latter alternative, there can be no defence of subsidising agriculture in such a way as this, without any control of how the funds are utilized, when much more precise methods of assistance might be employed.

Nevertheless, while most of these proposals are either unstable or uneconomic, the fact remains that there is considerable dissatisfaction among sections of the farming community, following the sequence of depression years, in which farm capital was often of necessity depleted, so that now farmers have not sufficient resources available to take advantage of improved conditions. While these complaints are undoubtedly well founded in certain cases, a large part of the discontent is based on an incomplete analysis of the essential problem. It is of little use obtaining credit to bolster up lines or methods of production which no longer pay. Generally speaking, the more substantial farmers have little difficulty in obtaining the accommodation they require. While for small "family farmers" the granting of more credit would not often mean a corresponding improvement in productive efficiency, but rather an additional millstone round their necks.

The conclusions arrived at in earlier chapters suggest that it is not so much working capital, as long-term investment which is needed at the present time, the kind of investment which landlords have found of late years increasingly difficult to undertake. The activities of the Agricultural Mortgage Corporation and the loans effected under the Land Improvement Act have been well adapted to their purposes, but they only touch the fringe of a much larger problem, the real nature of which we shall examine in the next chapter. Meanwhile, we believe that the supply of credit to working farmers will probably continue to be best operated through normal and accustomed channels.

CHAPTER XXI

LANDLORDS

Landlords' Functions

WHEN we come to consider the third partner in agriculture, we find a singular lack of statistical information as to the composition and distribution of the owners of land. Land is held by the State, by municipalities, by colleges, charitable institutions and banks as well as by private land-owners but, except in the case of public bodies, we do not know the size of their various estates, or how these are parcelled out, or under what conditions as to rent, length of tenancy they are held, or by what type of occupier they are cultivated. Nevertheless one can observe the changes, gradual but profound, affecting the landlord tenant system which have taken place during the last 100 years or so.

In the old days, leadership in farming was in the hands of the land-owner. He provided not only the land but the fixed capital including buildings, drainage and long-term improvements. This enabled the farmers to use their resources to finance their working expenses. The land-owner was responsible for many pioneer ventures in research and developments in the better cultivation of crops and the breeding of pedigree stock which in the 18th and early 19th centuries made British farming a model for the world.

The importation from abroad of food-stuffs in abundance marked the end of this era. From about 1870 agriculture ceased to expand, rents fell, whilst costs of maintenance increased. Capital now invested in the land earned a poor return compared with investments in industries. The former power and position of the land-owner were passing. Increased taxation and death duties added to his burdens. The ever-increasing death duties in particular had a disintegrating effect on the large estates, these duties being fundamentally irreconcilable with a system of large agricultural estates. The consequent decline in the fortunes of agriculture wrought great changes among the land-owning classes. There emerged the non-agricultural landlords—successful men in business and finance whose primary interests were in the amenities and not in agriculture and who had not always a strong sense of their obligations to the estate and their tenants.

The old agricultural landlords whose business was farming as well as land-owning were no longer able to sustain the burden of research and experimental work. Indeed, such work gradually passed into the hands of scientific institutions and research stations. The bulk of the more purely experimental work had become specialized to the chemist, the biologist, the physicist, and hosts of others, leaving the agriculturally-minded landlord with less scope for leadership in matters of technique. This slump had an important bearing on estate management as impoverished or small owners could not afford the type of scientifically trained business man required to supervise a large agricultural estate—other owners failed to realize the importance of having a fully qualified agent.

These difficulties found landlords not unwilling to sell their land to tenant-farmers; hence arose the large class of occupying-owners. Thirty years ago not more than 10 per cent. of the agricultural land was owned by occupiers; to-day, the proportion is probably about one-third. Many of these farmers bought their land at inflated prices after the War and saddled themselves with heavy mortgage interest payments. As between a mortgaged owner-occupier and a tenant renting from a landlord the position of the latter is in many respects preferable. The holder of a mortgage is the most absent of all absentee landlords and mortgage interest is likely to be much more inflexible than rent.

It is true that a farmer who has bought his farm outright enjoys certain advantages, but ownership makes heavy demands upon his available capital. There does not appear to be any widespread demand to-day on the part of farmers to own their farms. The landlord-tenant system is, or was, an effective compromise in that it enabled men with enterprise but with small capital to manage a farm of a more economic size than they could have obtained with their own capital alone.

Development of Tenant-right

One consequence of the decline in land-owners' capital resources was a gradual shifting of some of the provision of farm buildings, drainage and general improvements of a permanent character from the landlord to the tenant-farmer. When this tendency became particularly marked in the latter half of the 19th century, important questions arose as to the tenant's legal rights in respect of improvements made by him. He had, in fact, on giving up his tenancy, no right at common law to any claim against his landlord for buildings, fencing, drains, or any other improvements of a fixed character made by him. And he could not remove them. They were regarded as part of the land and became the property of the landlord. Under such a system there was little inducement to the tenant either to make or maintain any permanent improvements.

Such a state of affairs could not continue long. It is a matter of national interest that the land should be well cultivated and that, for this object, the actual cultivator should have security of tenure and full compensation for improvements made by him. Accordingly, a series of Agricultural Holdings Acts designed to achieve these objects were passed between 1883 and 1923.

These Acts entitle the tenant to compensation for improvements, freedom of cropping (i.e. freedom from the restrictive conditions in leases compelling the tenant to perform a certain rotation) and compensation for disturbance (i.e. for the cost of moving, if the landlord has served him with a notice to quit). This last right gives the tenant-farmer, in effect, as much security of tenure as is possible, short of ownership. As the compensation for disturbance may be as much as two years' rent, a landlord hesitates about getting rid of a bad tenant in a summary way. He can only get rid of an unsatisfactory tenant, without having to pay for "disturbance", on proving to the satisfaction of the County Agricultural Committee that the tenant is "not cultivating according to the rules of good husbandry". This has not worked efficiently. The landlord also may claim against the tenant for dilapidations to buildings, etc., as well as for injury to the land by bad farming. It is generally felt that the Acts shield bad farmers.

There is a further provision in this Act for arbitration in cases where the tenant has applied for a reduction of rent and the landlord has refused. Here again the number of cases dealt with is small.

In view of the many ways in which the law now safeguards the interests of the tenant, it might be supposed that he would tend to take over the functions no longer exercised by the landlord, and that agriculture would settle down to an equally satisfactory, if rather more lopsided, partnership. But this has only occurred to a limited extent. The long-drawn depression of British agriculture has affected farmers even more severely than landlords, and they have not been able to lay by enough savings to carry out those works of maintenance and improvements which would normally fall to the landlord. In consequence, estates have been allowed to run down, buildings have not been repaired, drains not relaid, farm roads not mended —all things which are at once seized upon by the critic as signs of general agricultural decay. It is easy to exaggerate the extent to which this has occurred, but there is little doubt that there has been a gradual wastage of much of the fixed capital of agriculture. Landlords no longer have resources equal to the task, tenant farmers are impoverished after years of falling prices and in any case require their savings to bring their own equipment into line with modern developments.

The Case for National Ownership

Accordingly, first in one way and then in another, the State itself has been obliged to take some of the responsibility which formerly devolved upon the landlord. It has given grants for experiment and research, and supplemented the work of the scientific agricultural institutions with advisory services. It set up a Livestock Improvement Commission with subsidies for stimulating the improvement of livestock. It set up the Agricultural Mortgage Corporation to enable farmers to become their own landlords and make long-term improvements. It has given subsidies for fertilizers and for drainage works, and we have seen in the preceding chapters how it has given considerable amounts of direct subsidies to agricultural products. To an ever-increasing extent public money is being used for tasks which in former times the landlords themselves would have accomplished.

It is becoming increasingly clear, however, that the need for land improvement and reorganization is as pressing to-day as ever it was and that the State will have to come forward with still more help. It is further coming to be realized that, to utilise to the utmost efficiency many of the chief mechanical appliances now available to agriculture, larger units of operation are required. But it is difficult to alter farm sizes while the land is in the hands of large numbers of different persons. And these considerations provide powerful arguments in favour of national ownership of the land.

The State, as landlord, would not suffer the disabilities of private landlords. It would be in a position to consider investment in the land from the point of view of the public interest and it would be able to initiate comprehensive land improvement schemes (e.g. large-scale drainage) which cannot easily be justified under present conditions. It could replace farm units. The State would be able to finance these improvements more cheaply than private enterprise by borrowing on long-term at low rates of interest. And the State would be in a better position to enforce standards of good cultivation upon its tenants. It would be able to accelerate the elimination of animal diseases and the up-grading of herds, and it would be able to offer as good if not better security of tenure, since there would be no eviction consequent upon selling up of estates.

There is a further point of importance. At present agricultural policy is cramped by the consideration that all financial assistance to farming whether given in the form of subsidy, import protection or derating tends in the long run to be a subsidy to the landed interest. Indeed, it is difficult to devise any scheme of which the benefit does not, in the long run, largely accrue to landlords in the shape of higher rents; and this is a formidable objection to any policy of agricultural subsidies, for the kinds of assistance which agriculture needs.

In principle, therefore, the arguments for the national ownership of agricultural land are overwhelmingly strong; and the circumstances of the coming years are likely to reinforce these arguments. On the other hand, there are important practical objections to any scheme for *wholesale* nationalization. Apart from the immense financial operation involved, it would entail a vast new administrative system. If the State assumes the role of landlord, it must leave a large degree of initiative and discretion to its local officers, a requirement alien to the tradition of public administration as hitherto evolved, and a new administrative technique would have to be built up. But if the change were brought about gradually there is no reason why the administrative problem should not be satisfactorily solved. The personnel of the administration could be found largely from the ranks of existing land-agents. The transfer of agricultural land to national ownership and administration is pre-eminently a case in which much would be gained by gradualness, and much would be lost by a sudden leap in the dark.

As a practical policy it would seem best to concentrate on taking over land where capital investment was most urgently required. A scheme could be devised whereby parcels of land could be transferred to public ownership from time to time, in convenient units for administration. Already, colleges and other public bodies enjoy a good reputation among tenants whilst the County Councils have acquired nearly half a million acres of land in this way for their small-holdings, but this provides a special service which should not be confused with a transference for a rather different purpose.

The Forestry Commission in another sphere is working smoothly.

Land Improvement Commission

What seems more needed is not indiscriminate acquisition by the State, but acquisition for the particular purpose of discharging certain necessary functions which are no longer discharged. Such a task might be assigned to a special Land Improvement Commission or preferably, perhaps to a regional system of Land Improvement Commissions. Where there was scope for the investment of additional capital on a substantial scale in landlords' improvements, the Commissions would be empowered to buy land. They would carry out a large variety of works including, for instance, renovation of farm buildings, land drainage, grassland regeneration. The last two are in many cases best and most cheaply carried out by the use of heavy and expensive equipment and specialised labour beyond the reach of the average farmer. Sometimes the land selected for acquisition might be an estate which was no longer being adequately maintained, sometimes it might be a particular area suitable for grassland improvement. The Commissions would stand in much the same relation to the tenant farmers as the County Councils, Smallholdings Committees do to smallholders.

The Commissions might recommend to the Government the acceptance of certain lands offered in lieu of death duties if suited to improvement purposes and an economical proposition; but the scheme should be left as flexible as possible since the over-riding consideration should be the maintenance and development of the agricultural estate.

Clearly, the work of the Land Improvement Commissions would develop slowly, so that it should be possible to avoid certain difficulties obviously associated with any wholesale nationalization; for instance, it should be possible to build up a trained staff of administrators who would compare in efficiency with the best landlords' agents and who would accumulate experience as the Commissions' work developed. In the course of time relatively large blocks of land would come under the Commissions' administration and in such areas it would be possible to consider the reorganization of farms into units of more economic size. It would be equally possible in such areas to experiment in really large-scale farming if conditions appeared favourable. In addition the Commissions, when handing land over to tenants could more easily than a private landlord insist on good cultivation as a condition of security of tenure; they could encourage the development of better quality live-stock, and generally exercise a beneficial influence on the standards of farming on their lands. The State instead of private landlords would benefit from such improvement or from that increased rental value inevitably resulting from present direct subsidies.

There appear, therefore, many arguments in favour of a development of policy along such lines as these, and moreover, there are reasonable prospects that such a policy would not involve serious political opposition. Indeed, it is likely that some steps in this direction will have to be taken before very long. Long term investment is not a task for farmers and it has ceased to be practicable for landlords. The logical development is for the State itself to take over suitable land where there is particular need for the maintenance of capital or scope for additional investment. Whereas the present policy of commodity subsidies leaves little of lasting value, the expenditure of public money on land improvement would create permanent capital assets besides providing farmers with what, in the long run, will probably prove the equipment most essential to successful competition in the conditions of the modern world.

CHAPTER XXII

RESEARCH, EDUCATION AND ADVICE

A National policy for agriculture must depend in the long run on what processes have become technically feasible and economically profitable. It should take account of the new possibilities which have been opened up by current scientific discoveries. So important have been these discoveries that the present era is sometimes referred to as the period of "The Second Agricultural Revolution", and the methods of farming evolved as a result of these discoveries are referred to as "The New Technique." But however important scientific research may be, knowledge of the new technique must be disseminated and widely practised in order to secure full benefit. The State accordingly lends a hand in promoting research and invention and in instructing farmers in up-to-date practice. It is clear that in many fields the new discoveries have hardly yet made themselves felt but in almost every instance the application of science to agriculture shows that less labour, land and perhaps capital are required to produce a given quantity of food than formerly.

Even before the Great War progress was considerable. In a group of American States the combined production of maize, wheat, oats and potatoes, increased by 70 per cent per acre. In Java the output of sugar per acre increased fourfold. In Denmark the livestock unit per 1,000 acres increased by 51 per cent. From 1914 onwards the progress all over the world in sugar, potatoes, wheat, vineyards, has been even more spectacular. Similarly cattle, pigs, cows, poultry have been improved enormously.

Engineering discoveries have replaced horse and hand labour by machinery.

Chemistry, too, is revolutionizing agriculture. Corn and maize in certain chemical solutions can be made to sprout artificially. It is even possible to grow crops without any land at all. In U.S.A., potatoes, tomatoes and other vegetables are grown indoors, their roots suspended in a chemical liquid. The yield of individual plants under this treatment surpasses many times anything ever recorded under natural conditions. The process is so far uneconomic on a commercial scale, but this may not always be so.

Agro-biology opens up further possibilities. Dr. Willcox has compared the maximum yields of stable crops with what he calls the "penultimate" yields, i.e. the theoretical maximum yield under optimum conditions, and finds the actual yield far below the theoretical. The penultimate yield of oats for instance is 395 bushels per acre, while the highest yield actually obtained from one acre has been 249 bushels. The British yield of roughly 40 bushels per acre is one-sixth of what has actually been grown and one-tenth of what theoretically might be. Even taking maximum actual yields and not the penultimate yield, the progress possible is startling. Taking only the known certified maximum yield per acre in the U.S.A. as a basis, the comparison with average yields shows that crops which now take 241 million acres could be grown on only 27 million acres. Obviously maximum yields could not be obtained all over the country but assuming that farmers reached 70 per cent of the maximum, the same output would be got from only 40 million acres—a little less than the area of the State of Kansas. The American farmer is not likely to attain this level for some time but if he doubled his present level (9 per cent of the maximum) all the staple crops could be grown on 120 million acres, or half the present area. That this increase is within reach cannot be doubted.

Under British conditions the potato illustrates the same potential development. Potatoes have been grown under special conditions at 50 tons per acre in Scotland. The average crop is 7–8 tons per acre. A mere rise of 25 per cent in output per acre would produce either a surplus over consuming power or reduce acreage by one-fifth. Since many farmers now produce 12–16 tons per acre the decline of acreage is sooner or later inevitable. Oats show a similar trend.

Another development is the treatment of grass by drying which opens up the possibility of providing a valuable foodstuff. Already in America by alternating wheat with Sudan grass and cutting and drying at early stages, 7 tons of hay per acre have been obtained containing nearly 2000 lbs. of proteins in addition to carbohydrates. This is nearly 1 ton of protein per acre, or twice as much as either of these plants could produce grown in ordinary rotation.

Without multiplying examples of what the application of science to agriculture has achieved, one can say that the danger of food scarcity has been overcome, and plenty is theoretically within the reach of all. Although vast areas of the earth have been wasted and eroded, there remain enough fertile acres, properly managed, to maintain the population on a fraction of the cultivable surface.

No matter what governments may do, new forces will sooner or later emerge. Science and the machine will gradually conquer the peasant, to his ultimate advantage and greatly to the advantage of the common man. But in the process there will be much whipping of dead horses, many casualties by the wayside, and much ignorance to be dispelled. The common man will look to the hill and say, "Ah, I remember that farm with four teams of horses he turns and looks into the valley he will forget to say, "Ah, and now there are only some sheep and a shepherd." But if I remember when that farm grew only five tons of potatoes and forty bushels of oats to the acre, and now it grows twenty tons and eighty bushels. I remember when it employed eighteen men and now there are only eight." So long as the importance of agriculture is judged by acreage under the plough and the number of men employed, and not by output, so long will uninformed interference in agriculture delay the greatest economic production and a rising standard of living. The political effects of the partial application of the " new technique " have escaped the notice of the public. It is the new knowledge of agricultural science which has enabled Germany, Italy and Japan to make those efforts at self-sufficiency in foodstuffs which contribute towards the present international crisis.

Agricultural Research in Britain

In Britain the State has recently appreciated the value of scientific research work. Various research institutions have been established, each generally specializing in some subject, and administered either independently or as a department of some university. These institutes receive Government grants amounting in all to just over £170,000 per annum. Most of them are also endowed from private or university sources. More than half the total sum goes to soils, crops and horticulture, even although the live-stock industry has for a long time been the predominant branch of British agriculture. But apart from the incongruous distribution of the funds, what is most striking is the insignificance of the total sum devoted by the State to agricultural research work. This may be partly because over a short period the results of expenditure may not be particularly evident, for discoveries often take years of apparently academic and unprofitable groping. It is important to realize the extent of experimental work in every branch of farming at the present time, some of which is undoubtedly destined to have a profound effect on agricultural technique.

In the sphere of plant-breeding the general aim is to increase productivity both in quantity and quality and to establish strains better adapted to various environmental factors. For instance, wheats are bred for grain composition, strength of straw, frost resistance, drought resistance, resistance to or immunity from diseases; grasses are bred for some of these characters but also for persistency, winter hardiness and so on. A successful combination of such characteristics may mean not only an increase of 10 or 20 per cent yield per acre, without any extra labour costs in cultivation, but also that a particular crop may be grown in areas from which it was previously excluded.

Work is being done on the environment of growing plants, on soils, fertilizers, methods of cultivation and management, with the problems of pasture environment: the manuring of grassland, the effects of grazing and manures on the composition of the herbage, the comparative effects of manuring and grazing on growth. It took the British farmer many decades to learn the value and proper use of artificial fertilizers; but recently, partly owing to the low price of fertilizers, he has used them more liberally and the total consumption is now 35 per cent higher than in 1913. But there is still the problem of efficiency of utilization of fertilizers: effective use is made of only a small part of the fetilizer used; the remainder appears to be lost, entering neither into the soil nor the crop.

There is also still the problem of organic manure, particularly farmyard manure, which appears irreplaceable on certain lands, but whose actual effects on the soil are imperfectly understood. The final elucidation of this problem will be of some importance for much of our mixed farming is carried on almost at a loss, largely in the belief that the land must have dung. Processes have also been evolved for converting town refuse and sewage into fertilizers.

An important line of research is that concerned with the breeding of cattle and animal nutrition. Breeding for performance has improved productive capacity enormously, though much can still be done. The best British breeding standards are excellent but the average of the rank and file is lamentably low. Equally promising is the study of live-stock feeding. The question of the causes and effects of malnutrition among animals is intimately associated with the quality of food-stuffs. The foods must come up to certain quality standards. The malnutrition of the animals may often be traced to mineral deficiency in the soil or the crop, which, when identified, can be made good. Just as with human beings, when we know how to feed the individual properly we shall have gone nearly halfway to conquering disease. Study is also attempting to discover what characters account for quality differences in our meat, butter, eggs, etc.

Meantime a frontal attack is being made on animal diseases at numerous stations. For bovine tuberculosis various vaccines have been produced, though none appear completely efficacious. Treatment for mastitis is still experimental. For Johne's disease, neither a method of detection nor treatment have yet been found satisfactory. More funds are needed for research into these diseases for by effectively tackling them milk yields can be increased and the herd life of the cow prolonged and consequently the cost of producing milk lowered. The ravages of disease have equally serious economic results in our poultry flocks, yet equally little is known about them or their cures. There is great need here for more experimental work and also for much more intelligent management by farmers.

Another aspect of developing the new technique is the steady introduction of machinery in all branches of agriculture—the tractor, the gyrotiller, the combine harvester, electrical milking machines and a range of more delicate implements which are conquering that last stronghold of manual labour—market gardening. In England and Wales the number of oil and petrol engines used on farms increased from 6,284 in 1913 to 65,725 in 1931, the last date for which figures are obtainable. The number of tractors has increased from 16,681 in 1925 to close on 40,000 in 1937. An indispensable adjunct to mechanization is electricity, yet several factors deter the farmer from using it—the cost of installation is often prohibitive, an advance estimate of the cost of current is difficult, and there are wide variations in tariff schedules between different districts. Until electricity is cheaper and sold at a uniform rate like petrol its use will be restricted. The adoption of all this labour saving machinery is a sign of progress and explains why a reduction in the numbers employed on the land does not prove ruin but may indicate real advance towards more economic output.

Enough has been said to give an idea of the main problems engaging the attention of agricultural research workers and of the developments in technique which are taking place. This is a field in which it would be relatively easy to justify spending much larger sums of money than are made available at present. In practice, it is necessary to decide on the relative urgency of various problems and to press for increased grants where new information is most definitely needed. At the present time it is plain that a great deal more work needs to be done on animal diseases. Among cattle alone the loss through disease costs farmers some £19 millions[1] a year. Although this branch of research has been extended, far more will have to be spent in the investigation of disease and other problems connected with live-stock. Practically the whole of British agriculture depends on our live-stock industry; until the animals are healthy, farming will not be healthy either.

Agricultural Education

However important scientific research may be, there is another equally important field of activity, the dissemination of the new technical knowledge among farmers and farm workers. Agricultural education in England is organized under three different authorities—the Ministry of Agriculture, the Board of Education and the County Councils. In Scotland the work is centralised through the Department of Health for Agriculture in three regional agricultural colleges, but in general the suggestions for improvement and extensions apply to both systems of organization.

There are the colleges or university departments specialized in agriculture, one in each of the eleven agricultural

[1] Loveday Committee on Veterinary Education.

I

provinces into which England and Wales is divided together with certain extra colleges for special purposes. These get between them block grants amounting to some £70,000 per annum. They have degree and diploma courses but only some 2,000 students take agricultural courses, and of these the bulk go into teaching, into the administrative service, or emigrate to the Dominions and colonies. This is partly because they have not sufficient capital to start farming on their own account and partly because there are scarcely any managerial posts on farms obtainable at home.

To each of these eleven centres is attached a staff of advisers to go about the countryside assisting farmers in their technical problems. Many are lamentably understaffed.

Apart from the colleges for students and the advisory staffs for farmers, almost all the agricultural education is carried out by the County Councils. The County Councils cater for some 22,000 students, of whom about half attend only evening classes. The staffs are general practitioners of agriculture who have to apportion their time between teaching, demonstration work and advice. They advise farmers on more general and sometimes elementary problems of farm organization than the provincial advisers.

The other main branch of activity of the County Agricultural Education Departments is the direction of Farm Institutes, which provide more systematic training than the itinerant educational staff can do, and combine it with practical work on the Institutes' farms. Unfortunately there are only about eighteen in England and Wales. The main course lasts from twenty to twenty-two weeks through the winter. Students of both sexes are resident and a typical institute will accommodate from thirty to forty at a time. The syllabus covers the usual practical subjects but concentrates on animal husbandry, including pigs, poultry and veterinary instruction, and on farm management, particularly book-keeping. There are usually shorter summer courses in dairying and horticulture.

What chiefly prevents more use being made of these institutes is the difficulty of distance. When an institute has to serve three or four counties it requires imagination and tenacity of purpose for a farmer to send his son for six months to attend a course some seventy miles away. More Institutes might create their own supply of students.

The County Council provides some 1,280 scholarships annually for courses at Institutes or Colleges whilst a certain amount of technical agricultural instruction is given in senior school and in continuation classes.

Besides the normal development of organized education there are other ways in which young people and farmers learn something of agricultural science. One such medium is the valuable organization known as Young Farmers' Clubs, with a membership at present of over 4,000. But for farm workers probably the most general source of information is the local press—where there are still undeveloped opportunities for spreading information. The radio too might become an important supplementary development.

Looked at as a whole, the system of agricultural education works somewhat unsatisfactorily and fails to produce the results it should. We are far from having as well-trained an agricultural community as should be possible with such a long-established educational organization. The new scientific knowledge is not being made adequately available to farmers. Agricultural research work has quite outstripped agricultural education; we want to get more effective steps taken to translate the knowledge of the few into the practice of the many. The knowledge is not getting through as well as it should and could. This is partly because not enough is spent on local demonstration plots, organized parties to experimental stations and publication of leaflets and pamphlets on current difficulties and partly is a result of defective organization.

There is a strong case for reorganizing all the different sections of agricultural education into a single system, operated from the provincial centres—colleges or university departments, whichever it may be. If these took over the work at present performed by the County Agricultural Education Departments, they would avoid overlapping and be in a position to pay better salaries and attract better men, and engage more specialists since they would be serving areas including not one but several counties. With one or two exceptions there are no specialists in particular crops or in live-stock management. Yet the farmer will seek and will heed the advice of a real specialist in, say, potato growing or pig rearing, cattle feeding, or soil fertility.

We believe that the modern knowledge would be put over more rapidly if in each area of suitable size, and in relation to the most important types of farming, there were stationed the appropriate specialists. In the great milk-producing areas there should be at least three specialists available for consultation—one on feeding and management of dairy cows, one on the management of grassland, and one on soil fertility; in the cattle feeding and arable areas one on the feeding of cattle, one on potato growing, one on grain production and one on pigs. Wales, the Border Country and the Highlands would give scope for specialists in sheep and wool.

Farm Institutes should also be set up in every county and developed into social centres for the agricultural community. The Farm Institute is one of the most neglected and most important links in the chain of agricultural education. It provides higher technical education for that majority section of the farming community which cannot afford the time or the money for a college course. It has the potentialities, more than any other existing institution, of developing along the lines of the Danish Folk High Schools and of creating a rural culture capable of holding its own, in its own way, with the urban culture of colleges and universities.

Such a system of Farm Institutes and of technical education under the control of the provincial centres would indirectly do much to increase the efficiency of the work of the Provincial Advisory Staffs. There would be more points of organized contact with farmers. But another of the major difficulties of the Advisory Staff, and especially of the advisory economists has been the lack of adequate statistics.

The farmer is under a statutory obligation to fill up on the 4th June every year a long and complicated return, yet it omits many points essential to the proper discussion of agricultural problems. The inadequacy of these returns is due to the insufficiency of the funds at the disposal of the Minister of Agriculture for collection of the returns.

These are some suggestions for improving the system of agricultural education and advice. The system at present is one of considerable complexity and we recognize that this very complexity renders difficult any thorough-going measure of reform.

At the same time, even though agricultural education is less cared for at the moment than agricultural research, and consequently deserves particular consideration, the research institution also needs help. It would be much better to err on the side of spending too much money on scientific experimental work rather than too little; every penny wisely laid out is a highly lucrative investment. It is better to help farmers by spending money on research than by giving direct subsidies to specific commodities. People almost always tend to ask for subsidies to enable them to carry on in the old traditional and often out-of-date way, when, otherwise, economic forces would have compelled them to make technical adjustments and march with the times. Moreover, a policy of subsidies to commodities creates new vested interests which naturally tend to safeguard themselves in every possible way by opposing changes. We have bad instances in the case of beet, sugar, bacon and milk products. A policy of subsidies to research and to education suffers from none of these disadvantages; it is incomparably more fruitful in the long run for agriculture as a whole; it will command a far wider measure of support, attracting the goodwill of the urban public as well as that of a large section of the farming community; it will benefit, most of all, those who wish to use up-to-date methods, whereas commodity subsidies cannot really avoid encouraging the inefficient along with the efficient.

In the light of these considerations there can be no doubt that a wise agricultural policy, worthy of the traditions of British farming, would provide for spending a great deal more on agricultural research, and, at the present time, particularly on the investigation of diseases of livestock. Britain was one of the first countries to apply science to agriculture; and in this new period of rapid technological change should be among the first countries adequately to foster the development of research.

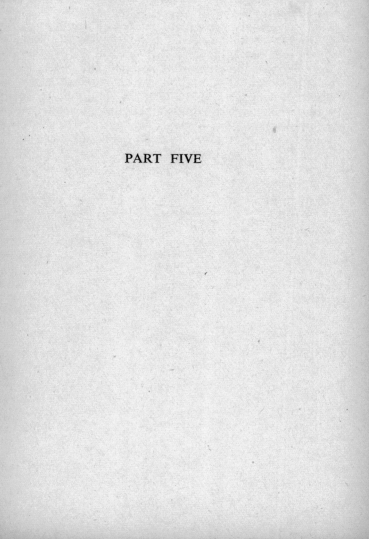

PART FIVE

PART FIVE

CHAPTER XXIII

CONCLUSIONS

Proposals summarized—National Policy of Improved Nutrition—Reconstitution of Marketing Boards—Acquisition of Agricultural Land through Land Improvement Commissions—Measures to Promote Efficiency—Revision of Existing Measures of Assistance—Need for Caution in this Revision—Agriculture not at present unduly Favoured—Complexity of Agricultural Economic Problems

WE have now completed our review of the economic problems of British agriculture. In the course of the preceding chapters we have made many suggestions of policy, some large and sweeping, others of a more limited and technical kind. We have been led to make our various suggestions mainly by the logic of the detailed circumstances of the particular agricultural problems we were considering, though we have had regard throughout to the governing principles which we formulated in our opening chapters. We shall now attempt to sum up the main features of the proposals we have made, and to add some supplementary observations.

We place in the forefront of our proposals the development of a national policy of improved nutrition. This represents in our judgment the most hopeful means of reconciling the objective of maintaining a substantial and prosperous agricultural industry with wider national purposes. From a broad sociological standpoint the improvement of the nutritional standards of the population is clearly marked out as the sphere of the next large advance in social policy. As regards education, housing, insurance against the risks of unemployment, sickness and old age, a system has been built up as the result of a long series of measures through which the efforts of individuals are supplemented by the organization and financial assistance of the State. It would be entirely appropriate, and given the maintenance of national economic progress, it would be perfectly feasible that a similar national effort should be made in the next generation to ensure that the health and vitality of the population are no longer impaired by inadequate or defective nourishment. From the agricultural standpoint an increased concentration on producing the "health-protective" food-stuffs is the most hopeful line of evolution for British farmers. For reasons which we have argued at length throughout this book, we do not believe that it will be possible, consistently with the pursuit of a wise international commercial policy, to find scope for an enlarged domestic production of staple food-stuffs such as wheat, meat, bacon, butter and cheese. But for producing many of the protective food-stuffs, British farmers enjoy a natural advantage as compared with overseas competition, which is not likely to be disturbed. A national nutritional policy may indeed provide the means not only of reconciling agricultural with wider national interests, but also of reconciling the interests of our own farmers with those of friendly agricultural communities overseas.

In practice the central feature of a constructive nutritional policy must be the promotion of the consumption of milk. This is the commodity, above all others, the consumption of which needs to be encouraged on nutritional grounds. It is also the commodity for producing which British agriculture enjoys the largest degree of natural protection. A wise national milk policy must embrace many features: propaganda, an improvement in quality, better methods of marketing and distribution. A practical step to which we attach importance is the de-control of the retail price of milk. But the policy must also include as an important element subsidies from the State in order to supply milk at specially cheap prices to school-children, to infants below school age and to expectant and nursing mothers. We do not think it appropriate to attempt to formulate a policy for promoting the consumption of milk in any detail. The administrative problems that would arise in this connection would carry us too far afield from the agricultural sphere. Moreover, the progress that can be made with any schemes entailing State financial assistance must obviously depend largely on the general condition of the national finances. We confine ourselves, therefore, to two further observations.

First, the potentialities of enlarging agricultural production by a successful policy of stimulating milk consumption are very large. The present average *per capita* consumption of milk by the British public is extremely low. If it were increased by one-third of a pint per day it would still be far below the level which is desirable on nutritional grounds and far below the level which is actually attained elsewhere, for instance in Sweden and the U.S.A. Clearly, therefore, there is nothing fantastic in formulating an increase of this magnitude as the ultimate goal of a national nutritional policy. Such an increase would, however, entail an expansion of our natural milk output of no less than 65 per cent. At the present rate of productivity this would require the maintenance of $2\frac{1}{2}$ million more cows.[1] This would represent a huge increase which could only be effected gradually and which would exert stimulating repercussions on ancillary branches of agriculture. If we could succeed in making steady progress towards this goal we could afford to contemplate a decline in the domestic production of agricultural commodities which can be most cheaply obtained from abroad, without anxiety lest this should entail injury to our agricultural life.

Our second observation relates to the question of cost. We contemplate, as we have already indicated, State subsidies for the purpose of supplying cheap milk for young children and expectant or nursing mothers. It is not easy to foresee how large such subsidies would require to be to achieve their object, nor is it easy to estimate the net addition to consumption that subsidies of a given magnitude would produce. It is important to remember, however, that the Exchequer at present provides substantial subsidies, notably in connection with beet sugar and meat

[1] For further discussion of this aspect see: Prof. H. D. Kay "National Nutrition and British Agriculture: Increased Production of Milk." *Scottish Journal of Agriculture*. January 1937.

for the benefit of agriculture. It would be reasonable and appropriate, in our judgment, that these subsidies should be reduced and eventually perhaps abandoned if a steady expansion in the consumption of milk could be effected by a nutritional policy. It is by no means out of the question that by such an exchange agriculture might derive substantial net benefit without any material increase in the expenditure borne by the State. From the agricultural standpoint, moreover, such an exchange would have the advantage that the State assistance given for the purpose of improving the health and nutrition of the population at large would be far less likely to be cut down in times of financial difficulty than subsidies which were of benefit to agriculturalists alone.[1]

Our second main proposal, though we suggest it for general application, is also of especial practical importance in regard to milk. We urge that the constitution of the marketing boards which administer the various statutory marketing-schemes should be transformed. We recommend that these boards should be appointed by the appropriate departments of State to represent the public interest. This is a reform which in our judgment is essential, if agricultural marketing is to evolve on satisfactory lines. The present system under which important statutory powers, which include the fixing of the prices that must be paid by the consuming public, are entrusted to bodies which are elected by and responsible only to producers is an anomaly which is indefensible in principle and unsatisfactory in practice. It encourages the pursuit of a wrong aim—the fixing of prices at the highest level which is considered prudent, instead of the cheapening of costs and the stimulation of demand. It is an obstacle to the adoption of a national policy of improved nutrition. It may prove a source of friction between the farming community and the industrial population. The most recent developments

---

[1] A complete nutrition policy would also include measures to stimulate the consumption of the other protective foods: fruit, vegetables and eggs.

in the sphere of marketing policy indicate, indeed, some appreciation of the need for modifying the existing arrangements. There is a clearly marked tendency to subject elected marketing boards to supervision and control by Commissions appointed to represent the public interest, and it seems probable that this principle will shortly be applied to the marketing of milk. Progress along these lines undoubtedly represents, from the political standpoint, an easier line of approach than the more radical re-organization that we advocate, and it is possible that the new Commissions may do something to ensure a greater regard for the public interest in the determination of price and in other aspects of marketing policy. None the less the machinery of elected boards controlled by public Commissions is cumbrous and is not likely, we believe, to work satisfactorily in practice. There is no reason, other than the prior existence of the producer-elected marketing boards, why two different sets of bodies with different responsibilities and perhaps divergent aims should be charged with the administration of the statutory marketing schemes. The simpler principle which we recommend is, it may be observed, that upon which the Ulster Milk Board is based. It would be far easier to develop constructive schemes for stimulating an increased consumption of milk and other protective foods, or for improving the system of retail distribution, if the powers of the marketing boards were in the hands of bodies representative of the public interest. We regard the reconstruction of the marketing boards on these lines as an essential feature of a wise agricultural policy.

Our third main proposal is that a regional system of Land Improvement Commissions should be established to acquire agricultural land on which there is need for long-term capital improvements. In making this proposal we have not been moved by any preconceived ideas on the merits of nationalization; we have been rather driven to it by the logic of agricultural facts. We are impressed with the evidence that an increasing number of landlords are unable to discharge effectively their historic function of supplying agriculture with the long-term capital improvements which it requires. We are impressed, on the other hand, with the need and opportunity for greater capital in many sections of farming. But our proposal that the State should, through the instrument of a system of public utility concerns, come gradually to assume on a considerable scale the role of agricultural landlord, is in harmony with the general trend of evolution in the functions of the State. In the coal industry, for example, after much hesitation and delay, the State has adopted the position of royalty owner. It has thus established with the coal industry a relationship in some respects similar to that which we propose in the case of agriculture. It is true, of course, that the nationalization of agricultural land is a far larger and more complex matter than the nationalization of coal. For this reason we suggest that the State should proceed on cautious and tentative lines, acquiring land only in cases where there is a clear need and profitable opportunity for expenditure. In other words the transference to national ownership should, in our view, only be made where there is a function to be discharged which is not at present effectively discharged.

We believe that the relationship between the State and agriculture that would thus be established would be an appropriate one. The role of landlord would enable the State to influence the evolution of agricultural structure in directions that seemed desirable, to encourage, for example, the amalgamation of holdings into larger farming units in cases where this is advisable on technical grounds. It would enable the State to insist on standards of good farming, to aid enterprising farmers in adopting new methods or applying the results of scientific research and generally to encourage all schemes tending to improve the quality of British produce and to promote productive and marketing efficiency. This is the kind of function which the State, we believe, can advantageously discharge.

This proposal has a bearing on wider questions of national policy which it may be of interest to consider. One of the main objects of the Land Improvement Commissions, according to our plan, would be to undertake long-term improvements. In raising the capital required, they would be backed by the credit of the State, so that agriculture would obtain the long-term capital required for its development on advantageous terms. This would be of obvious benefit to agriculture. But it might also be of advantage to the State that a larger proportion of the capital expenditure of the community should come in this way under its control. In recent years the idea of regulating or stimulating expenditure on public works so as to offset the fluctuations of industrial activity or to promote recovery from depression has become a major question of economic policy both in this country and abroad. In the event of another serious depression, it is virtually certain that this question will come again into the foreground of discussion; that demands will be made for large public works programmes; and that the Government, whatever its complexion, will at least do its utmost to press forward any form of capital expenditure for which substantial economic justification can be claimed. It might in these circumstances be of some assistance to public policy, if there was a considerable amount of work that could be put in hand by our proposed Land Improvement Commissions for the better equipment of agriculture. The fact that much of the work would consist of a heterogeneous mass of individually small improvements might even be an advantage in this connection. Large public-works projects take a long time to prepare and a long time to execute; and it is difficult in practice to speed them up or slow them down so as to fit in with the needs of the trade situation. In the case of much of the work that Land Improvement Commissions might be expected to undertake, this difficulty would not be so serious.

We do not wish to overstate the point that we are making. It is unlikely that the contribution which the capital equipment of agriculture could make to a programme of public-works expenditure in a period of depression would be of major importance. But it would at least be helpful; and this fact is pertinent for two reasons. First, it indicates that our proposal is in harmony rather than in conflict with the broader requirements of national economic policy. Secondly, it suggests that the State could reasonably afford to advance money to the Land Improvement Commissions at a low rate of interest, and that if the average yield obtained by the Commissions were to fall somewhat below the rate at which the Government had to borrow, the loss incurred by the State might be merely nominal. On the grounds that increased employment will entail a saving in unemployment benefit and an increase in the yield of taxes, public-works projects, which are only partially remunerative, are advocated in times of depression as sound propositions from the financial standpoint of the State. If these arguments are valid, they apply to capital expenditure on agricultural improvements. The advance of money on cheap terms to Land Improvement Commissions would thus represent one of the least costly ways in which the State could give assistance to agriculture.

We turn to proposals of a different type. We have laid great stress throughout this book on measures which are likely to increase efficiency. We have made suggestions for improving our arrangements with regard to agricultural research, education and technical advice. More liberal financial provision is needed for research work both into the technical and economic problems of agriculture. It is no less important to secure that existing and fresh scientific knowledge is made available to the farmer, and for this purpose we have suggested that the educational and advisory services should be developed and placed under the control of the provincial centres. We have urged much more energetic attempts to eradicate animal disease, which according to an informed estimate costs the country about £19 million a year. A beginning has already been made by the centralization of the veterinary services and by the new grants made for the investigation of disease; the proposals of the Poultry Technical Committee also advocate development in this direction. We consider that still more vigorous measures will prove necessary;

not merely research into the nature of diseases and into vaccines and other methods of cure, but also a tightening up of regulations regarding the breeding and distribution of stock—for instance, in the poultry industry by reforming the Accredited Breeders' Scheme.

We have stressed the importance of improving the quality of the product in many branches of farming. For example, in milk production we advocate a raising of the minimum hygiene requirements; indeed we would like to see all milk below accredited standard within a short time banished from the liquid raw milk market. In beef production we noted a need for greater emphasis upon quality, and to this end the Licensing of Bulls Act should be made more effective and supplemented by a more extensive development of the premium bulls scheme. The pig industry would benefit from similar steps for improvement.

Besides this we have supported measures tending to maintain and improve the fertility of the soil. We welcome, in principle, the assistance given to farmers to purchase artificial manures. We would like to see greater emphasis laid upon the creation of good grassland and upon the technique of its management, partly by increased financial support and partly by educational work through the advisory services; for we believe that grass is the most important "crop" in this country and that a large acreage of well-kept grassland would provide invaluable stores of fertility which might be cashed in time of emergency. For all these purposes we should be ready to contemplate a considerable increase in the financial assistance provided by the State, believing that in the long run a given sum of money spent wisely in such ways will be of substantially greater benefit to agriculture than a similar sum doled out in subsidies to commodities which this country is not naturally well fitted to produce.

In laying such stress upon efficiency, we recognize that we expose ourselves to the possibility of misapprehension and perhaps of some not unnatural resentment. The average man knows that in any walk of life people are never as efficient as they might be and that it is always desirable that they should become more efficient. He knows that in any department of affairs people are always to be found who urge that efficiency might be greatly increased by some new expedient or administrative change; that these people are sometimes right and sometimes wrong; but that the layman can hardly ever judge. The general public are, accordingly, inclined to greet proposals for increased efficiency with the same attitude of benevolent apathy that they extend to expressions of sentiments which are unexceptional but platitudinous.

The average farmer, on the other hand, is inclined to retort that he knows as well as his critics that it is important to be efficient, and that he does his best to be so; but that dinning this into his ears does nothing to help him. If you are engaged in a hard struggle with adverse conditions and are exposed to the risk of serious loss and perhaps disaster from vicissitudes which are outside your control, nothing is more annoying than to hear it suggested by outsiders, who may be imperfectly acquainted with your circumstances, that your difficulties would be solved by an improvement in your efficiency. Least of all can the farmer be expected to welcome any suggestion that increased State assistance for purposes likely to improve efficiency should be gradually substituted for subsidies which are unlikely to promote this object.

Despite these considerations, we are convinced that the promotion of efficiency must be a central feature of a constructive agricultural policy; and we think it desirable in this concluding chapter to recapitulate the main reasons which have led us to take this view. In the first place there has never, perhaps, been a time in which the opportunities for improving agricultural efficiency were so many and so various as they are to-day. In the eighteenth and nineteenth centuries the methods of manufacture and transportation were revolutionized by a remarkable series of inventions which so impressed the public imagination that the process is commonly named the industrial revolution. During this period agricultural technique was by no means stagnant. But it seemed so in contrast to the amazing rate of technical progress in industry, and the mental habit grew up of thinking of agricultural methods as though they were rigid and unchanging, and as though the process of invention and discovery was virtually limited to the industrial sphere. In the past generation this situation has been completely transformed. Applied science is now making some of its most conspicuous advances in the sphere of agricultural production. The engineer, the chemist, the biologist are all contributing in their different fields to increase the volume of agricultural output that a given amount of human labour can produce: and it seems probable that in the last few decades the rate of technical progress in the Western world has been at least as rapid in agricultural production as in industry. These conditions constitute at once an opportunity and a challenge to British agriculture. There is no reason why the average farmer should not approximate more nearly to the methods, knowledge and skill of the best British farmers, and consequently why our farmers, as a whole, should not be again in the future, as they were until modern times, in the van of technical progress. There are, indeed, some indications which encourage the hope that in some branches at least British agriculture may re-assume the role of leadership.

It is only, we believe, through a steady increase in efficiency that we can hope to secure an expanding market for British agricultural produce. As we have seen repeatedly throughout this book the quality of the product supplied is of the first importance if the British public is to be induced to buy more of it. If the British product is of inferior quality or represents poor value for money, the utmost stimulus to demand that can be given by protective measures or subsidies is apt to prove disappointing. On the other hand, given products of high quality, a steadily expanding market for many agricultural commodities can reasonably be expected, provided that their selling prices are kept reasonably low. To improve the quality of British agricultural products, and to maintain low selling prices in face of the rising tendency that must be expected in labour costs, there is need for constant attention to efficiency in production and marketing.

It would be unfortunate, therefore, if the non-agricultural public were to treat the emphasis we have laid upon efficiency as though it were merely a pious platitude. We need throughout the community a truer and keener appreciation of the large possibilities which the present state of agricultural science opens up. Among the farmers we need, as indeed we are beginning to obtain, a spirit of greater responsiveness to the stirrings of technical change. We need a greater, more continuous and more cordial co-operation between the State and the farming community in the improvement of farming methods. On these conditions we may eventually achieve a real marriage between nutrition and agriculture which may represent one of the most important developments of the next generation.

Another class of proposals to which we attach importance are measures to improve the conditions of life of the agricultural workers. On general grounds it is desirable that so far as possible they should receive equality of treatment with industrial workers in the matter of housing, health services, education facilities, and so forth. It is also desirable from the farmers' point of view. Labour is becoming increasingly scarce on the land, not only because farmers cannot pay wages as high as other industries pay, but also because of the unsatisfactory nature of the living conditions of the workers. Measures designed to improve the position of the farmer will be largely nullified if he cannot get labour; he will find it increasingly difficult to obtain labour unless rural conditions are rapidly improved.

We should like to see a far more vigorous rural housing policy than that envisaged in the 1938 Act and with a more adequate rate of subsidy. In the past the needs of rural workers have been too often subordinated to those of the urban population and at the present time there is an undeniable shortage of decent housing accommodation in rural areas. We should like to see more rapid progress made with the provision of water supply in rural areas. We have also made recommendations for improving health services and educational facilities, in particular for the grouping of primary schools in rural areas into larger units and making general the practice of transporting children to and from school by motor-bus where distances are great. Much has been done by voluntary organizations to improve the amenities of rural districts; much also has been accomplished by local authorities; but the present need is for improvements which can only be undertaken with increased assistance from the central government.

The foregoing represent our major positive proposals. On the other hand we have taken the line that several experimental policies that have been pursued in recent years with the object of stimulating particular branches of agriculture should be revised. We do not believe that the attempt to establish a beet sugar industry in Great Britain by means of heavy subsidies can be permanently justified. We consider that the guaranteed price for wheat was fixed at too high a level and has resulted in an unjustifiable expansion in production. We believe that it would be unwise to persist in the attempt to establish a substantial British bacon industry by measures which entail the restriction of imports from Denmark and other countries. Nor in our judgment is there an adequate case for maintaining the subsidy for beef-cattle on its present lines. The practical objection to all these experiments is the same, that they throw a burden on the Exchequer or on the consumers, or do other damage to the national interests, which is out of proportion to the benefit they bring to farmers. In each case this practical objection springs from the same fundamental cause; namely that the branch of agriculture which these experiments are designed to foster is one in which British farmers are at a heavy natural disadvantage as compared with producers overseas. Under existing technical conditions cane-sugar can be produced much more economically in tropical countries than beet sugar can be produced in Europe. Similar considerations apply to the attempts artificially to foster wheat production. Countries like Denmark which have a long-established bacon industry, closely associated with butter making, have a competitive advantage for the supply of good quality bacon to the British market, which as experience shows, it is not easy to overcome. For beef production parts of Australia and Argentina derive from cheap land and rich natural pastures a competitive advantage which seems likely to be reinforced by further advances in refrigeration technique. It is, we believe, fundamentally false policy to seek to counter natural advantages such as these. To do so is to repudiate the principle of the international division of labour in precisely the applications where it offers the greatest benefits. It cannot be reconciled with a rational approach to the problems of international trade.

We do not suggest, however, that these experiments should be suddenly scrapped, that the beet sugar or cattle subsidies should be immediately withdrawn or that imports of bacon should at once be freed from quantitative limitation. There are two considerations in this connection to which regard must be paid. In the first place it is important, amid the uncertainties of the world agricultural outlook, to avoid any steps that might entail serious disturbance in particular branches of agriculture or in particular rural areas, or a decline in the volume of agricultural production as a whole. This consideration alone would make it wise to proceed gradually with the revision of measures which have been of substantial benefit to British farmers in the emergency difficulties of recent years.

In the second place our fiscal system is no longer based upon Free Trade. Import duties are now levied upon the majority of manufactured goods; and in some important cases, e.g. iron and steel, the rates of duty are high. In principle, agriculture has a claim to a degree of State assistance similar to that which is extended to industry in general, the whole structure of British prices has necessarily been affected by the introduction of Protection. The prices which farmers must pay for tractors, ploughs and wire-netting, and which they and their labourers must pay for industrial products they consume, are higher than they would be under Free Trade. If in these circumstances agriculture were left to meet overseas competition without any protection, it would be artificially handicapped.

How, then, does the State assistance given to agriculture, compare with that enjoyed by manufacturing industries? This is a question upon which it is important to form as just an idea as possible. We have given a detailed account of most of the measures of assistance in our chapters dealing with the different agricultural commodities. We can best convey an impression of their aggregate effects by a summary in tabular form.

Commodity	Duties on imports from Foreign Countries. (Specific Duties expressed as Ad Valorem equivalent, using 1938 prices) %	Subsidies	Other Measures
Beef and Veal	10–20	Cattle subsidy costing about £5 million	Quantitative limitation of imports; voluntary from Empire countries, and compulsory from foreign countries
Canned beef and other sorts	10		
Mutton and Lamb			Quantitative limitation of imports
Pork			Do.
Bacon		Subsidy in form of Deficiency Payments to Curers, costing about £1 million per annum	Statutory Marketing Scheme and Quantitative Limitation of Imports
Butter	11–14	*Deficiency Payments from Exchequer when butter and cheese prices below certain level	
Cheese	15		
Milk		Manufacturing subsidy and subsidies to improve quality* and increase demand costing from, say, £2 million to £4 million per year	Statutory Marketing Scheme

Commodity	Duties on imports from Foreign Countries. (Specfic Duties expressed as Ad Valorem equivalent, using 1938 prices) %	Subsidies	Other Measures
Condensed Milk	15		Quantitative limitation of imports by agreement
Poultry (dead)	25		
Eggs in shell	10–15		
Eggs not in shell	5–20		
Wheat	5	Levy-subsidy scheme operating in accordance with the price-level costing £1 million to £5 million per annum.	
Barley meal	20	Exchequer subsidy operating in accordance with price of oats, and costing about £1¾ million per annum	
Oats	35–40		
Potatoes (New)	20–25		Compulsory quantitative limitation of imports; and statutory marketing scheme
Potatoes (Other)	20–30		
Hops	95		Statutory marketing scheme, with prohibition of new entrants and with import quota
Sugar	220	Subsidy and revenue abatement together costing about £5 million to £6 million per annum	
Fruit	15–20†		
Vegetables	15–20†		
Fertilizers	20‡		
Feeding-stuffs	10§		
Agricultural implements and machinery	20–33		

* Proposed; not yet in operation (August, 1938).

† According to type of fruit (or vegeteble) and time of year.
‡ Mineral phosphates of lime, Kainite and Nitrate of lime are duty-free.
§ Maize, cotton-seed and rape-seed are duty-free. Soya beans and meal pay 20 per cent.

The tariff rates refer, it should be noted, to imports from foreign countries. Imports from Empire countries are free of duty in every case, except hops and sugar; in the case of hops, imports from Empire countries pay two-thirds of the full duty; in the case of sugar, one-half. The subsidies listed include only those paid in respect of particular agricultural commodities. In addition, the State pays subsidies, costing £1 million per annum, to cheapen the price to farmers of lime and basic slag and has recently agreed to pay £2 per acre for the renovation by cultivation of old grassland. It spends some £600,000 per annum on the improvement of herds and the eradication of animal disease; and a further £600,000 on research and advisory services. Farmers also, of course, derive substantial pecuniary benefits from the derating scheme and from special income-tax arrangements.

It is obviously impossible to reduce these various forms of assistance to any common measure. The significance of the schemes for the quantitative restriction of imports varies greatly from case to case, and is complicated by the Imperial Preference *motif*. The benefits which farmers derive at the expense of the consumer from the levy-subsidy scheme for wheat depend entirely on the movement of world prices. It will be observed, however, that the subsidies which fall on the Exchequer irrespective of the level of world prices are limited to those for cattle and milk.

In considering the protection accorded to agriculture by means of import duties it is essential to bear in mind one vital point. As already stated imports of agricultural products from Empire sources are admitted free of duty in every case except those of hops and sugar. Now the agricultural producers of the British Dominions and Colonies are among the British farmers' most formidable competitors. In this respect agriculture is in sharp contrast to the manufacturing industry. The effective protection enjoyed by the majority of manufacturers on the commodities they produce is fairly indicated by the rates of duties imposed on imports from foreign countries. But this is not true of agriculture. In a few cases British producers derive a material benefit from the duties on foreign imports and in some of these cases, e.g. fruit and vegetables, the rates of duty are higher than can easily be justified. In the main, however, the agricultural tariffs and quotas on foreign imports are ineffective as a means of assisting the British farmer owing to the free admission of imports from Empire sources. It is, indeed, mainly for this reason that other steps have been taken to assist British farmers in the case of such important commodities as wheat and beef.

We think it well to emphasize this point since it is, we believe, insufficiently appreciated. Calculations are frequently made in which the duties imposed on imports of agricultural products from foreign countries are treated as though they were equivalent to cash subsidies to the British farmers, and are lumped together with the subsidies actually paid by the Exchequer so as to produce a huge aggregate figure of State assistance. The impression is conveyed that agriculture receives about the same measure of protection against overseas competition that is enjoyed by industry by means of ordinary tariffs, and is then accorded large supplementary assistance by subsidies and in other ways. Nothing could be more misleading than such calculations or more unfair than this impression. British agriculture derives comparatively little benefit from import duties on the commodities that it produces. It is adversely affected by substantial import duties on many commodities which it buys. The State subsidies, the quota schemes for limiting imports and the other measures of assistance, are to be regarded as so many steps taken, not to place agriculture in a pampered and privileged position, but to hold even the balance which would otherwise be tilted heavily against agriculture. For this purpose these measures, though open to serious criticism in detail, are not, we believe, excessive or extravagant in their total effects.

This consideration has an important bearing on the manner in which the question of revising the existing measures of agricultural assistance should be approached. We believe that the proposals which we have made in this book and have summarized in the present chapter, are capable, when fully developed, of conferring on agriculture a greater benefit than it derives at present from the measures we have criticized. But this is a belief to which some uncertainty must necessarily attach. Some of the more important of our proposals only lend themselves to gradual application. The extent, for example, to which the production of milk would be stimulated by a national policy of nutrition must depend on the character of that policy; and this is a matter on which, inasmuch as it raises administrative and social questions lying outside the agricultural sphere, we have not attempted to make detailed suggestions.

But agriculture is entitled in our judgment to a continuance of State assistance in one form or another, on roughly the present scale. While, therefore, we look for a gradual reduction in the State assistance at present given in respect of wheat, beet sugar, beef and bacon, as progress is made in the directions we advocate, we consider it essential that the extent of the reductions made under the former head should be governed by the progress made under the latter.

We are convinced on the other hand, that those are profoundly mistaken who aim at effecting an expansion of British agriculture by further measures of protection against overseas competition or by further subsidies for commodities which can be produced considerably more cheaply or more efficiently abroad. Our national interests in the maintenance of a large-scale international trade, the interests of the consuming population in the provision of cheap food, the interests of the British Dominions and Colonies as agricultural producers, the growing budgetary difficulties of the British Treasury, the complications of the structure of British agriculture itself, combine to render any such policy the height of unwisdom. The aims of our agricultural policy should be to promote a happy marriage between nutrition and agriculture rather than to shut out overseas competition, to improve the conditions of the agricultural labourers rather than to increase their numbers, to treat agriculture as an industry or group of industries, possessing peculiar features indeed, but existing for the purpose of satisfying human wants with the minimum of toil, rather than as a way of life to be preserved with the minimum of change.

It is impossible to study the economic problems of British agriculture without being impressed by their complexity. In some degree their complexity explains the miscellaneous nature of the expedients which represent the treatment of agriculture by the State. This heterogeneity of treatment adds greatly in turn to the complications of the problems that now exist. It has become extremely difficult for the intelligent layman to form a clear grasp of the issues involved. He is confused by a bewildering mass of detail, in which unifying principle or illuminating generalizations are hard to discover.

For this reason, the disinterested public attention that is given to agricultural questions is apt to be far less than their intrinsic importance deserves. The evolution of agricultural policy raises issues which are of vital concern to the future well-being of society. Yet it is difficult to suppose that they will be handled wisely without the aid of a keenly interested and well-informed public opinion. It is in the hope that it may contribute to the development of this public opinion that this book has been written.

S P R I N G

Last April, a man was drilling 7 acres of barley with 2 horses. He finished at 4.45. I brought my Fordson to his field that evening. With a double set of horse harrows, 18 feet wide, I went over the whole field in one hour, using 1½ gallons of paraffin. A few days later I ploughed 12 acres of land in two days. It was a race against time, and I was never more glad to have Fordson power with me.

FORDSON TRACTOR

Completely built at Dagenham, England.

Your Fordson Dealer will demonstrate.

FORD MOTOR COMPANY LIMITED, DAGENHAM, ESSEX, AND 88 REGENT STREET, LONDON, W.1

SUMMER

I had a difficult harvest time two years back. At the crucial moment I had a field of corn laid low by wind and rain. My son got to work with the Fordson, worked all day and well into the night and again the next day and managed to cut the whole field. Immediately a fortnight's rain followed, which would have spoilt the crop completely. I bought a new Fordson out of the money I saved on that crop!

FORDSON TRACTOR

Completely built at Dagenham, England.

Your Fordson Dealer will demonstrate.

FORD MOTOR COMPANY LIMITED, DAGENHAM, ESSEX, AND 88 REGENT STREET, LONDON, W.1